CARNEGIE LEARNING
LONG + LIVE + MATH

Middle School Math Solution
Course 2

Student Edition
Volume 1

Sandy Bartle Finocchi and Amy Jones Lewis

with Kelly Edenfield and Josh Fisher

CARNEGIE LEARNING

501 Grant St., Suite 1075
Pittsburgh, PA 15219
Phone 888.851.7094
Customer Service Phone 412.690.2444
Fax 412.690.2444

www.carnegielearning.com

Cover Design by Anne Milliron

ISBN: 978-1-68459-286-9
Student Edition, Volume 1

Printed in the United States of America
1 2 3 4 5 6 7 8 9 BB 21 20

LONG + LIVE + MATH

Acknowledgments

Middle School Math Solution Authors

- Sandy Bartle Finocchi, Senior Academic Officer
- Amy Jones Lewis, Director of Instructional Design
- Kelly Edenfield, Instructional Designer
- Josh Fisher, Instructional Designer

Foundation Authors (2010)

- William S. Hadley, Algebra and Proportional Reasoning
- Mary Lou Metz, Data Analysis and Probability
- Mary Lynn Raith, Number and Operations
- Janet Sinopoli, Algebra
- Jaclyn Snyder, Geometry and Measurement

Vendors

- Lumina Datamatics, Ltd.
- Cenveo Publisher Services, Inc.

Images

- www.pixabay.com

Special Thanks

- Alison Huettner for project management and editorial review.
- Jacyln Snyder and Janet Sinopoli for their contributions to the Teacher's Implementation Guide facilitation notes.
- Victoria Fisher for her review of content and contributions to all the ancillary materials.
- Valerie Muller for her contributions and review of content.
- The members of Carnegie Learning's Cognitive Scientist Team—Brendon Towle, John Connelly, Bob Hausmann, Chas Murray, and Martina Pavelko—for their insight in learning science and review of content.
- Bob Hausmann for his contributions to the Family Guide.
- John Jorgenson, Chief Marketing Officer, for all his insight and messaging.
- Carnegie Learning's Education Services Team for content review and providing customer feedback.
- In Memory of David Dengler, Director of Curriculum Development (Deceased), who made substantial contributions to conceptualizing Carnegie Learning's middle school software.

"Mathematics is so much more than memorizing rules. It is learning to reason, to make connections, and to make sense of the world. We believe in Learning by Doing(TM)—you need to actively engage with the content if you are to benefit from it. The lessons were designed to take you from your intuitive understanding of the world and build on your prior experiences to then learn new concepts. My hope is that these instructional materials help you build a deep understanding of math."

Sandy Bartle Finocchi, Senior Academic Officer

"My hope is that as you work through this course, you feel capable—capable of exploring new ideas that build upon what you already know, capable of struggling through challenging problems, capable of thinking creatively about how to fix mistakes, and capable of thinking like a mathematician."

Amy Jones Lewis, Director of Instructional Design

"At Carnegie Learning we have created an organization whose mission and culture is defined by your success. Our passion is creating products that make sense of the world of mathematics and ignite a passion in you. Our hope is that you will enjoy our resources as much as we enjoyed creating them."

Barry Malkin, CEO

Table of Contents

Module 1: Thinking Proportionally

Topic 1: Circles and Ratio

1.1 Pi: The Ultimate Ratio
Exploring the Ratio of Circle Circumference to Diameter M1-7

1.2 That's a Spicy Pizza!
Area of Circles...M1-19

1.3 Circular Reasoning
Solving Area and Circumference Problems M1-33

Topic 2: Fractional Rates

2.1 Making Punch
Unit Rate Representations M1-51

2.2 Eggzactly!
Solving Problems with Ratios of Fractions M1-59

2.3 Tagging Sharks
Solving Proportions Using Means and Extremes...M1-69

Topic 3: Proportionality

3.1 How Does Your Garden Grow?
Proportional Relationships...M1-91

3.2 Complying with Title IX
Constant of Proportionality..M1-109

3.3 Fish-Inches
Identifying the Constant of Proportionality in Graphs.....................................M1-127

3.4 Minding Your Ps and Qs
Constant of Proportionality in Multiple Representations..............................M1-139

Topic 4: Proportional Relationships

4.1 Markups and Markdowns
Introducing Proportions to Solve Percent Problems......................................M1-161

4.2 Perks of Work
Calculating Tips, Commissions, and Simple Interest M1-177

4.3 No Taxation Without Calculation
Sales Tax, Income Tax, and Fees..M1-197

4.4   More Ups and Downs
Percent Increase and Percent Decrease M1-209

4.5   Pound for Pound, Inch for Inch
Scale and Scale Drawings M1-223

Module 2: Operating with Signed Numbers

Topic 1: Adding and Subtracting Rational Numbers

1.1   Math Football
Using Models to Understand Integer Addition M2-7

1.2   Walk the Line
Adding Integers, Part I..M2-17

1.3   Two-Color Counters
Adding Integers, Part II...M2-31

1.4   What's the Difference?
Subtracting Integers M2-49

1.5   All Mixed Up
Adding and Subtracting Rational Numbers..M2-69

Topic 2: Multiplying and Dividing Rational Numbers

2.1   Equal Groups
Multiplying and Dividing Integers M2-89

2.2   Be Rational!
Quotients of Integers..M2-103

2.3   Building a Wright Brothers' Flyer
Simplifying Expressions to Solve Problems M2-113

2.4   Properties Schmoperties
Using Number Properties to Interpret Expressions with Signed Numbers...M2-125

Module 3: Reasoning Algebraically

Topic 1: Algebraic Expressions

1.1   No Substitute for Hard Work
Evaluating Algebraic Expressions M3-7

1.2   Mathematics Gymnastics
Rewriting Expressions Using the Distributive Property....................................M3-19

1.3   All My Xs
Combining Like Terms M3-33

Topic 2: Two-Step Equations and Inequalities

2.1 Picture Algebra
     Modeling Equations as Equal Expressions M3-53

2.2 Expressions That Play Together...
     Solving Equations on a Double Number Line M3-65

2.3 Formally Yours
     Using Inverse Operations to Solve Equations M3-77

2.4 Be Greater Than
     Solving Inequalities with Inverse Operations...M3-95

Topic 3: Multiple Representations of Equations

3.1 Put It on the Plane
     Representing Equations with Tables and Graphs M3-125

3.2 Stretches, Stacks, and Structure
     Structure of Linear Equations..M3-139

3.3 Deep Flight I
     Building Inequalities and Equations to Solve Problems M3-155

3.4 Texas Tea and Temperature
     Using Multiple Representations to Solve Problems...................................M3-169

Module 4: Analyzing Populations and Probabilities

Topic 1: Introduction to Probability

1.1 Rolling, Rolling, Rolling...
     Defining and Representing Probability...M4-7

1.2 Give the Models a Chance
     Probability Models...M4-23

1.3 Toss the Cup
     Determining Experimental Probability of Simple Events...........................M4-33

1.4 A Simulating Conversation
     Simulating Simple Experiments M4-47

Topic 2: Compound Probability

2.1 Evens or Odds?
     Using Arrays to Organize Outcomes M4-73

2.2 Three Girls and No Boys?
     Using Tree Diagrams..M4-89

2.3 Pet Shop Probability
Determining Compound Probability M4-101

2.4 On a Hot Streak
Simulating Probability of Compound Events..................................M4-113

Topic 3: Drawing Inferences

3.1 We Want to Hear From You!
Collecting Random Samples..M4-133

3.2 Tiles, Gumballs, and Pumpkins
Using Random Samples to Draw Inferences...................................M4-151

3.3 Spicy or Dark?
Comparing Two Populations...M4-169

3.4 Finding Your Spot to Live
Using Random Samples from Two Populations to Draw Conclusions M4-181

Module 5: Constructing and Measuring

Topic 1: Angles and Triangles

1.1 Here's Lookin' at Euclid
Geometric Constructions..M5-7

1.2 Special Delivery
Special Angle Relationships..M5-19

1.3 Consider Every Side
Constructing Triangles Given Sides..M5-39

1.4 Unique or Not?
Constructing Triangles Given Angles..M5-53

Topic 2: Three-Dimensional Figures

2.1 Slicing and Dicing
Cross-Sections of Rectangular Prisms...M5-75

2.2 Dissecting a Pyramid
Cross-Sections of Rectangular Pyramids...M5-97

2.3 Hey, Mister, Got Some Bird Seed?
Volume of Pyramids...M5-107

2.4 The Sound of Surface Area
Surface Area of Pyramids...M5-129

2.5 More Than Four Sides of the Story
Volume and Surface Area of Prisms and Pyramids M5-143

Glossary G-1

Index I-1

1. Learning Goals

Learning goals are stated for each lesson to help you take ownership of the learning objectives.

2. Connection

Each lesson begins with a statement connecting what you have learned with a question to ponder.

Return to this question at the end of this lesson to gauge your understanding.

Stretches, Stacks, and Structure

2

Structure of Linear Equations

WARM UP

Use properties to rewrite.

1. $3(x - 1)$

2. $-9(-2 + x)$

3. $\frac{1}{2}(x - 6)$

4. $6 + 3(x + 4)$

LEARNING GOALS ①

- Write and solve two-step equations.
- Compare two linear problem situations.
- Rewrite expressions in different forms in problem contexts in order to interpret how quantities are related.
- Compare graphs of linear problem situations.
- Compare and interpret forms of linear equations.

 All of the linear equations you have written for problem situations have been in the form $y = ax + b$. Are there other common forms of equations used to express linear problem situations?

LESSON 2: Stretches, Stacks, and Structure • M3-139

3. Getting Started
Each lesson begins
with a Getting Started.
When working on
the Getting Started,
use what you know
about the world, what
you have learned
previously, or your
intuition. The goal is
just to get you thinking
and ready for what's to
come.

③ Getting Started

Learning the Limo Business

Katie is starting her own limousine rental company. She wisely decides to check her competitors' pricing plans before setting her own plan. The table shows the fees from two rival limousine rental companies.

Examine the fee schedule for the two limousine companies provided in the table.

Number of Hours Rented	Limousines by Lilly Fees (in dollars)	Transportation with Class Fees (in dollars)
1	99.99	89.99
2	123.74	126.54
3	147.49	163.09
4	171.24	199.64
5	194.99	236.19

1. Which company would you choose if you were renting a limousine? Support your answer with information from the table.

4. Activities

You are going to build a deep understanding of mathematics through a variety of activities in an environment where collaboration and conversations are important and expected.

You will learn how to solve new problems, but you will also learn why those strategies work and how they are connected to other strategies you already know.

Remember:

- It's not just about answer-getting. The process is important.

- Making mistakes is a critical part of learning, so take risks.

- There is often more than one way to solve a problem.

Activities may include real-world problems, sorting activities, worked examples, or analyzing sample student work.

Be prepared to share your solutions and methods with your classmates.

---

4 | ACTIVITY **2.1** | Different Forms, Same Equation

Katie starts by analyzing the cost structure of Limousines by Lilly.

1. Cons... by Li...

   a. Wr... by...

   b. W... Li...

   c. W... for...

   d. W... for...

   e. Ex...

ACTIVITY **2.2** | Comparing Graphs of Linear Equations

Your job at Storage Pros is to create new boxes to ship the

ACTIVITY **2.3** | Interpreting Forms of Equations

In the limousine and container scenarios, you represented the situations with two different equations.

1. Complete the table to summarize the different forms of the equations. Use the variables x and y for the independent and dependent variables.

	$y = ax + b$	$y = c + d(x - 1)$
Limousines by Lilly		$y = 99.99 + 23.75(x - 1)$
Transportation with Class		
Round Containers	$y = 0.8x + 8.2$	
Square Containers		

2. Use your equations to explain the meaning of the c and d terms in $y = c + d(x - 1)$.

3. Use your equations to explain the meaning of the a and b terms in $y = ax + b$.

Any letter can be used as a variable. It is common to use a and b in forms of equations, but the different variables were used to reduce the possibility of confusing the equations.

5. Talk the Talk
Talk the Talk gives you an opportunity to reflect on the main ideas of the lesson.

- Be honest with yourself.
- Ask questions to clarify anything you don't understand.
- Show what you know!

Don't forget to revisit the question posed on the lesson opening page to gauge your understanding.

NOTES

⑤ TALK the TALK

Back to the Limos!

At the beginning of the lesson, you wrote equations for the fee schedule of Limousines by Lilly and Transportation with Class.

1. Determine which graph represents each equation. Use your equations to explain your reasoning.

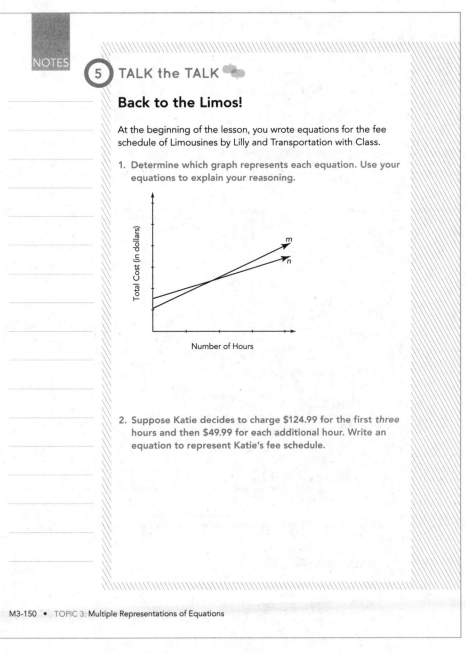

Number of Hours

2. Suppose Katie decides to charge $124.99 for the first *three* hours and then $49.99 for each additional hour. Write an equation to represent Katie's fee schedule.

Assignment

6. Write
Reflect on your work and clarify your thinking.

7. Remember
Take note of the key concepts from the lesson.

8. Practice
Use the concepts learned in the lesson to solve problems.

9. Stretch
Ready for a challenge?

10. Review
Remember what you've learned by practicing concepts from previous lessons and topics.

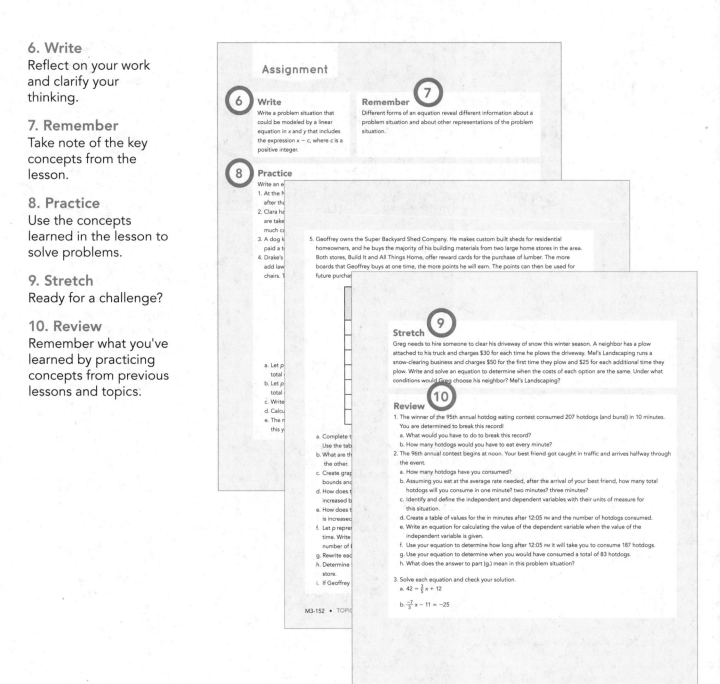

Assignment

6 Write
Write a problem situation that could be modeled by a linear equation in x and y that includes the expression $x - c$, where c is a positive integer.

Remember 7
Different forms of an equation reveal different information about a problem situation and about other representations of the problem situation.

8 Practice
Write an e...
1. At the N...
   after tha...
2. Clara ha...
   are take...
   much ca...
3. A dog k...
   paid a t...
4. Drake's...
   add law...
   chairs. T...

5. Geoffrey owns the Super Backyard Shed Company. He makes custom built sheds for residential homeowners, and he buys the majority of his building materials from two large home stores in the area. Both stores, Build It and All Things Home, offer reward cards for the purchase of lumber. The more boards that Geoffrey buys at one time, the more points he will earn. The points can then be used for future purcha...

a. Let p...
   total...
b. Let p...
   total...
c. Write...
d. Calcu...
e. The r...
   this y...

a. Complete t...
   Use the tab...
b. What are th...
   the other.
c. Create grap...
   bounds and...
d. How does t...
   increased b...
e. How does t...
   is increasec...
f. Let p repres...
   time. Write...
   number of...
g. Rewrite eac...
h. Determine...
   store.
i. If Geoffrey...

Stretch 9
Greg needs to hire someone to clear his driveway of snow this winter season. A neighbor has a plow attached to his truck and charges $30 for each time he plows the driveway. Mel's Landscaping runs a snow-clearing business and charges $50 for the first time they plow and $25 for each additional time they plow. Write and solve an equation to determine when the costs of each option are the same. Under what conditions would Greg choose his neighbor? Mel's Landscaping?

Review 10
1. The winner of the 95th annual hotdog eating contest consumed 207 hotdogs (and buns!) in 10 minutes. You are determined to break this record!
   a. What would you have to do to break this record?
   b. How many hotdogs would you have to eat every minute?
2. The 96th annual contest begins at noon. Your best friend got caught in traffic and arrives halfway through the event.
   a. How many hotdogs have you consumed?
   b. Assuming you eat at the average rate needed, after the arrival of your best friend, how many total hotdogs will you consume in one minute? two minutes? three minutes?
   c. Identify and define the independent and dependent variables with their units of measure for this situation.
   d. Create a table of values for the in minutes after 12:05 PM and the number of hotdogs consumed.
   e. Write an equation for calculating the value of the dependent variable when the value of the independent variable is given.
   f. Use your equation to determine how long after 12:05 PM it will take you to consume 187 hotdogs.
   g. Use your equation to determine when you would have consumed a total of 83 hotdogs.
   h. What does the answer to part (g.) mean in this problem situation?

3. Solve each equation and check your solution.
   a. $42 = \frac{3}{5}x + 12$

   b. $\frac{-7}{3}x - 11 = -25$

M3-152 • TOPIC

LESSON 2: Stretches, Stacks, and Structure • M3-153

WORKED EXAMPLE

$$\frac{11}{3}x + 5 = \frac{17}{3} \qquad\qquad \frac{1}{2}x + \frac{3}{4} = 2$$

Step 1: $\quad 3\left(\frac{11}{3}x + 5\right) = 3\left(\frac{17}{3}\right) \qquad 4\left(\frac{1}{2}x + \frac{3}{4}\right) = 4(2)$

Step 2: $\quad 11x + 15 = 17 \qquad\qquad 2x + 3 = 8$

Step 3: $\qquad\qquad x = \frac{17 - 15}{11} \qquad\qquad x = \frac{8 - 3}{2}$

$$= \frac{2}{11} \qquad\qquad\qquad\qquad = \frac{5}{2}$$

Worked Example

When you see a Worked Example:
- Take your time to read through it.
- Question your own understanding.
- Think about the connections between steps.

Ask Yourself:
- What is the main idea?
- How would this work if I changed the numbers?
- Have I used these strategies before?

Thumbs Up

When you see a Thumbs Up icon:
- Take your time to read through the correct solution.
- Think about the connections between steps.

Ask Yourself:
- Why is this method correct?
- Have I used this method before?

Thumbs Down

When you see a Thumbs Down icon:
- Take your time to read through the incorrect solution.
- Think about what error was made.

Ask Yourself:
- Where is the error?
- Why is it an error?
- How can I correct it?

Analyze the solution strategy and solution for each inequality.

Ella

$$-\frac{1}{2}x + \frac{3}{4} < 2$$

$$-4\left(-\frac{1}{2}x + \frac{3}{4} < 2\right)$$

$$2x - 3 > -8$$

$$2x > -5$$

$$x > \frac{-5}{2}$$

$$x > -2.5$$

Describe the strategy that Ella used correctly.

Jeff

$$-12x + 20 < 32$$

$$\frac{-12x + 20}{-4} < \frac{32}{-4}$$

$$3x - 5 < -8$$

$$3x < -3$$

$$x < -1$$

Identify the error in Jeff's strategy and determine the correct solution.

Who's Correct

When you see a Who's Correct icon:

- Take your time to read through the situation.
- Question the strategy or reason given.
- Determine correct or not correct.

Ask Yourself:

- Does the reasoning make sense?
- If the reasoning makes sense, what is the justification?
- If the reasoning does not make sense, what error was made?

Vanessa was given a math problem to determine how many different rectangles can be constructed with an area of 12 square inches.

Vanessa thinks that there are only two: one with a width of 2 inches and a length of 6 inches, and another with a width of 3 inches and a length of 4 inches.
Is she correct? Explain your reasoning.

The Crew is here to help you on your journey. Sometimes they will remind you about things you already learned. Sometimes they will ask you questions to help you think about different strategies. Sometimes they will share fun facts. They are members of your group—someone you can rely on!

Teacher aides will guide you along your journey. They will help you make connections and remind you to think about the details.

Habits of Mind

Mathematical Practices

The types of activities within this book require you to make sense of mathematics and to demonstrate your reasoning through problem solving, writing, discussing, and presenting. Effective communication and collaboration are essential skills of a successful learner.

Each activity is denoted with an icon that represents a practice or pair of practices intentionally being developed. To help develop these habits of mind ask yourself the types of questions listed as you work.

With practice, you can develop the habits of mind of a productive mathematical thinker.

▶ Make sense of problems and persevere in solving them.

This practice is evident every day in every lesson. No icon used.

Questions to ask:

- What is this problem asking and what is my plan for answering it?
- What tools do I need to solve this problem?
- Does my answer make sense?

▶ Reason abstractly and quantitatively.
▶ Construct viable arguments and critique the reasoning of others.

Questions to ask:

- What representation can I use to solve this problem?
- How can this problem be represented with symbols and numbers?
- How can I explain my thinking?
- How does my strategy compare to my partner's?

> I hope that every once in a while you will see something that you weren't quite expecting. These are my favorite parts! Because I <3 being confused at first, and then figuring it out.
>
> Josh Fisher, Instructional Designer

▶ **Model with mathematics.**
▶ **Use appropriate tools strategically.**

Questions to ask:

- What expression or equation could represent this situation?
- What tools would help me solve this problem?
- What representations best show my thinking?
- How does this answer make sense in the context of the original problem?

▶ **Attend to precision.**

Questions to ask:

- Is my answer accurate?
- Did I use the correct units or labels?
- Is there a more efficient way to solve this problem?
- Is there more sophisticated vocabulary that I could use in my explanation?

▶ **Look for and make use of structure.**
▶ **Look for and express regularity in repeated reasoning.**

Questions to ask:

- What characteristics of this expression or equation are made clear through this representation?
- How can I use what I know to explain why this works?
- Can I develop a more efficient method?
- How could this problem help me to solve another problem?

"This book is your place to record your thoughts, your conjectures, your mistakes, your strategies, and your 'ah-has' about the mathematics you need to learn this year. Don't erase when you make mistakes; cross it out so that you can still see your original thinking. Learn from your mistakes and grow your brain.

Kelly Edenfield, Instructional Designer

Academic Glossary

There are important terms you will encounter throughout this book. It is important that you have an understanding of these words as you get started on your journey through the mathematical concepts. Knowing what is meant by these terms and using these terms will help you think, reason, and communicate your ideas.

ANALYZE

Related Phrases

- Examine
- Evaluate
- Determine
- Observe
- Consider
- Investigate
- What do you notice?
- What do you think?
- Sort and match

Definition

To study or look closely for patterns. Analyzing can involve examining or breaking a concept down into smaller parts to gain a better understanding of it.

Ask Yourself

- Do I see any patterns?
- Have I seen something like this before?
- What happens if the shape, representation, or numbers change?

EXPLAIN YOUR REASONING

Related Phrases

- Show your work
- Explain your calculation
- Justify
- Why or why not?

Definition

To give details or describe how to determine an answer or solution. Explaining your reasoning helps justify conclusions.

Ask Yourself

- How should I organize my thoughts?
- Is my explanation logical?
- Does my reasoning make sense?
- How can I justify my answer to others?

REPRESENT

Definition

To display information in various ways. Representing mathematics can be done using words, tables, graphs, or symbols.

Ask Yourself

- How should I organize my thoughts?
- How do I use this model to show a concept or idea?
- What does this representation tell me?
- Is my representation accurate?

Related Phrases

- Show
- Sketch
- Draw
- Create
- Plot
- Graph
- Write an equation
- Complete the table

ESTIMATE

Definition

To make an educated guess based on the analysis of given data. Estimating first helps inform reasoning.

Ask Yourself

- Does my reasoning make sense?
- Is my solution close to my estimation?

Related Phrases

- Predict
- Approximate
- Expect
- About how much?

DESCRIBE

Definition

To represent or give an account of in words. Describing communicates mathematical ideas to others.

Ask Yourself

- How should I organize my thoughts?
- Is my explanation logical?
- Did I consider the context of the situation?
- Does my reasoning make sense?

Related Phrases

- Demonstrate
- Label
- Display
- Compare
- Determine
- Define
- What are the advantages?
- What are the disadvantages?
- What is similar?
- What is different?

MODULE 1

THINKING PROPORTIONALLY

The lessons in this module build on your experiences with ratios and proportional relationships from grade 6. You will investigate special ratios to develop and connect formulas for the circumference and area of circles. You will identify and describe proportional and non-proportional mathematical and real-world situations to understand the characteristics of proportional relationships. You will then use formal strategies to solve proportion and percent problems.

Topic 1 Circles and Ratio M1-3

Topic 2 Fractional Rates M1-47

Topic 3 Proportionality M1-87

Topic 4 Proportional Relationships M1-157

Circles and Ratio

Dropping something into water causes a series of ripples to expand from the point of impact, forming concentric circles.

Lesson 1
Pi: The Ultimate Ratio
Exploring the Ratio of Circle Circumference to Diameter M1-7

Lesson 2
That's a Spicy Pizza!
Area of Circles M1-19

Lesson 3
Circular Reasoning
Solving Area and Circumference Problems M1-33

Module 1: Thinking Proportionally

TOPIC 1: CIRCLES AND RATIO

In this topic, students learn formulas for the circumference and area of circles and use those formulas to solve mathematical and real-world problems. To fully understand the formulas, students develop an understanding of the irrational number pi (π) as the ratio of a circle's circumference to its diameter. Throughout the topic, students practice applying the formulas for the circumference and area of a circle, often selecting the appropriate formula. Finally, students practice applying the formulas by using them to solve a variety of problems, including calculating the area of composite figures.

Where have we been?

Throughout elementary school, students used and labeled circles and determined the perimeters of shapes formed with straight lines. In grade 6, students worked extensively with ratios and ratio reasoning. To begin this topic, students draw on these experiences as they use physical tools to investigate a constant ratio, pi.

Where are we going?

This early review of and experience with ratios prepares students for future lessons where they will move from concrete representations and reasoning about ratios and proportions to more abstract and symbolic work with solving proportions and representing proportional relationships. In future grades, students will use the circumference and area formulas of a circle to calculate surface areas and volumes of cylinders and composite three-dimensional shapes that include circles.

Modeling the Area of a Circle Using Wedges

Divide a circle into a large number of equal-sized wedges. Laying these wedges as shown, you can see that they approximate a rectangle with a length of πr and a height of r. The more wedges are added, the closer the figure will be to an exact rectangle. So, the rectangle of wedges, and thus, the circle, each has an area of πr^2.

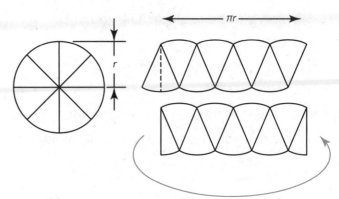

Myth: "I don't have the math gene."

Let's be clear about something. There isn't *a* gene that controls the development of mathematical thinking. Instead, there are probably **hundreds** of genes that contribute to our ability to reason mathematically. Moreover, a recent study suggests that mathematical thinking arises from the ability to learn a language. Given the right input from the environment, children learn to speak without any formal instruction. They can learn number sense and pattern recognition the same way.

To further nurture your child's mathematical growth, attend to the learning environment. You can think of it as providing a nutritious mathematical diet that includes discussing math in the real world, offering the right kind of encouragement, being available to answer questions, allowing your student to struggle with difficult concepts, and giving them space for plenty of practice.

#mathmythbusted

Talking Points

You can further support your student's learning by asking questions about the work they do in class or at home. Your student is learning to think flexibly about mathematical relationships involving multiplication, area, and number properties.

Questions to Ask

- How does this problem look like something you did in class?
- Can you show me the strategy you used to solve this problem? Do you know another way to solve it?
- Does your answer make sense? How do you know?
- Is there anything you don't understand? How can you use today's lesson to help?

Key Terms

radius
The radius of a circle is a line segment formed by connecting a point on the circle and the center of the circle.

diameter
The diameter of a circle is a line segment formed by connecting two points on the circle such that the line segment passes through the center point.

circumference
The circumference of a circle is the distance around the circle. The circumference is calculated using the formula $C = \pi d$.

pi
The number pi (π) is the ratio of the circumference of a circle to its diameter.

Pi: The Ultimate Ratio

1

Exploring the Ratio of Circle Circumference to Diameter

WARM UP

Scale up or down to determine an equivalent ratio.

1. $\dfrac{18 \text{ miles}}{3 \text{ hours}} = \dfrac{?}{1 \text{ hour}}$

2. $\dfrac{\$750}{4 \text{ days}} = \dfrac{?}{1 \text{ day}}$

3. $\dfrac{12 \text{ in.}}{1 \text{ ft}} = \dfrac{?}{5 \text{ ft}}$

4. $\dfrac{48 \text{ oz}}{3 \text{ lb}} = \dfrac{?}{1 \text{ lb}}$

LEARNING GOALS

- Identify pi (π) as the ratio of the circumference of a circle to its diameter.
- Construct circles using a compass and identify various parts of circles.
- Know and write the formula for the circumference of a circle, and use the formula to solve problems.

KEY TERMS

- congruent
- circle
- radius
- diameter
- circumference
- pi

You have learned about ratios. How can you use ratios to analyze the properties of geometric figures such as circles?

Across and Around

A circle is shown with a point drawn at the center of the circle. The name of the point is O, so let's call this Circle O.

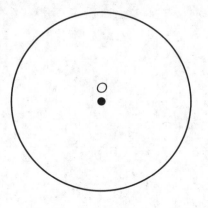

> Be sure to include units when you record your measurements.

1. Analyze the distance around the circle.

   a. Use a string and a centimeter ruler to determine the distance around the circle.

   b. How does your measurement compare to your classmates' measurements? Summarize the similarities and differences.

2. Draw a line from a point on the circle to the center of the circle, point O.

   a. Measure your line using your centimeter ruler.

   b. How does your measurement compare to your classmates' measurements? Summarize the similarities and differences.

Everyone can identify a circle when they see it, but defining a circle is a bit harder. Can you define a circle without using the word *round*? Investigating how a circle is formed will help you mathematically define a circle.

1. Follow the given steps to investigate how a circle is formed.

Step 1: In the space provided, draw a point and label the point *A*.

Step 2: Use a centimeter ruler to locate and draw a second point that is exactly 5 cm from point *A*. Label this point *B*.

Step 3: Locate a third point that is exactly 5 cm from point *A*. Label this point *C*.

Step 4: Repeat this process until you have drawn at least ten distinct points that are each exactly 5 cm from point *A*.

2. How many other points could be located exactly 5 cm from point *A*? How would you describe this collection of points in relation to point *A*?

3. Define the term *circle* without using the word *round*.

A **circle** is a collection of points on the same plane equidistant from the same point. The center of a circle is the point from which all points on the circle are equidistant. Circles are named by their center point.

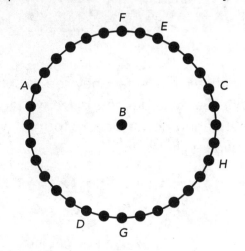

4. Use the circle shown to answer each question.

   a. Name the circle.

The **radius** of a circle is a line segment formed by connecting a point on the circle and the center of the circle. The distance across a circle through the center is the diameter of the circle. The **diameter** of a circle is a line segment formed by connecting two points on the circle such that the line segment passes through the center point. The distance around a circle is called the **circumference** of the circle.

   b. Identify a radius of the circle.

The plural of *radius* is *radii*.

   c. Identify a diameter of the circle.

   d. Are all radii of this circle the same length? Explain your reasoning.

5. What is the relationship between the length of a radius and the length of a diameter?

Measuring the Distance Around a Circle

Let's explore circles. Use circles *A*, *B*, *D*, *E*, and *O* provided at the end of the lesson. Circle *O* is the same as the circle from the activity *Across and Around*.

1. Use a string and a centimeter ruler to measure the distance from a point on the circle to the center and the distance around each circle. Record your measurements in the table. In the last column, write the ratio of *Circumference : Diameter* in fractional form.

Circle	Circumference	Radius	Diameter	$\dfrac{\text{Circumference}}{\text{Diameter}}$
Circle *A*				
Circle *B*				
Circle *O*				
Circle *D*				
Circle *E*				

2. Average the ratios recorded for $\dfrac{\text{Circumference}}{\text{Diameter}}$. What is the approximate ratio for the circumference to the diameter for the set of circles? Write the approximate ratio as a fraction and as a decimal.

3. How does your answer to Question 2 compare to your classmates' answers?

4. Average all of your classmates' answers to Question 3. Write the approximate ratio of circumference to the diameter as a fraction and as a decimal.

NOTES

The number **pi** (π) is the ratio of the circumference of a circle to its diameter. That is pi $= \frac{\text{circumference of a circle}}{\text{diameter of a circle}}$, or $\pi = \frac{C}{d}$, where C is the circumference of the circle, and d is the diameter of the circle. The number π has an infinite number of decimal digits that never repeat. Some approximations used for the value π are 3.14 and $\frac{22}{7}$.

1. Use this information to write a formula for the circumference of a circle, where d represents the diameter of a circle and C represents the circumference of a circle.

2. Rewrite the formula for the circumference of a circle, where r represents the radius of a circle and C represents the circumference of a circle.

3. Use different representations for π to calculate the circumference of a circle.

   a. Calculate the circumference of a circle with a diameter of 4.5 centimeters and a circle with a radius of 6 inches. Round your answer to the nearest ten-thousandths, if necessary.

Value for π	d = 4.5 centimeters	r = 6 inches
π		
Use the π Key on a Calculator		
Use 3.14 for π		
Use $\frac{22}{7}$ for π		

b. Compare your circumference calculations. How do the different values of π affect your calculations?

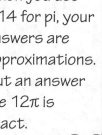

When you use 3.14 for pi, your answers are approximations. But an answer like 12π is exact.

4. Use the circumference of a circle formula to determine each unknown. Use 3.14 for π.

a. Compute the diameter of the circle with a circumference of 65.94 feet.

b. Compute the radius of the circle with a circumference of 109.9 millimeters.

5. What is the minimum amount of information needed to compute the circumference of a circle?

TALK the TALK

Twice

Use what you have learned to compare circles by their characteristics.

1. Draw each circle.

    a. radius length of   b. diameter length of
       3 centimeters   3 centimeters

2. Describe the similarities and differences between your two circles.

3. Describe the relationship between the circumferences of the two circles.

4. Describe the circumference-to-diameter ratio of all circles.

Measuring the Distance Around a Circle

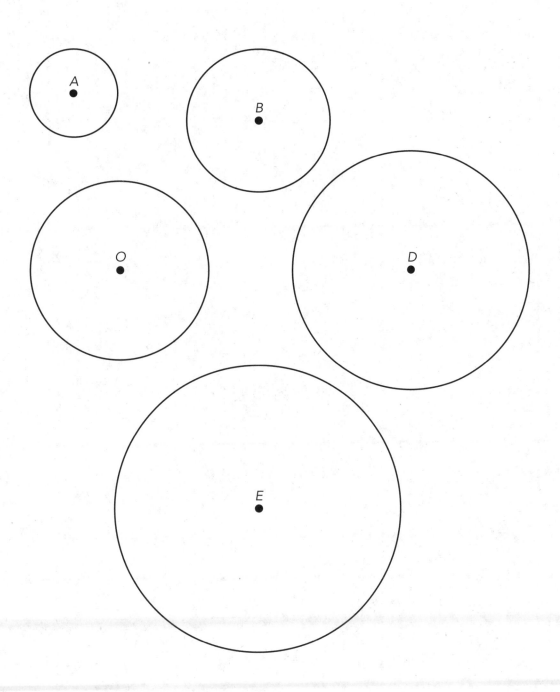

Assignment

Write

Define each term in your own words.

1. circle
2. radius
3. diameter
4. pi

Remember

The circumference of a circle is the distance around the circle. The formulas to determine the circumference of a circle are $C = \pi d$ or $C = 2\pi r$, where d represents the diameter, r represents the radius, and π is a constant value equal to approximately 3.14 or $\frac{22}{7}$.

The constant pi (π) represents the ratio of the circumference of a circle to its diameter.

Practice

Answer each question. Use 3.14 for π. Round your answer to the nearest hundredth, if necessary.

1. Although she's only in middle school, Tameka loves to drive go-carts! Her favorite place to drive go-carts, Driver's Delight, has 3 circular tracks. Track 1 has a radius of 60 feet. Track 2 has a radius of 85 feet. Track 3 has a radius of 110 feet.

   a. Compute the circumference of Track 1.

   b. Compute the circumference of Track 2.

   c. Compute the circumference of Track 3.

   d. Driver's Delight is considering building a new track. They have a circular space with a diameter of 150 feet. Compute the circumference of the circular space.

2. Tameka wants to build a circular go-cart track in her backyard.

   a. If she wants the track to have a circumference of 150 feet, what does the radius of the track need to be?

   b. If she wants the track to have a circumference of 200 feet, what does the radius of the track need to be?

   c. If she wants the track to have a circumference of 400 feet, what does the diameter of the track need to be?

Stretch

A rope is arranged using three semi-circles to form the pattern shown. Determine the length of the rope.

8 in.   3 in.   8 in.

Review

1. Ethan and Corinne are training for a marathon.

   a. Corinne runs 13.5 miles in 2 hours. What is her rate?

   b. Ethan wants to run the 26.2 miles of the marathon in 4.5 hours. At about what rate will he have to run to reach this goal? Round to the nearest tenth.

2. Fifteen seventh graders were randomly selected to see how many pushups in a row they could do. Their data are shown.

   45, 40, 36, 38, 42, 48, 40, 40, 70, 45, 42, 43, 48, 36

   a. Determine the mean of this data set.

   b. Determine the median of this data set.

3. Convert each measurement.

   a. $4\frac{1}{2}$ pounds = _____ oz

   b. 22.86 cm = _____ in.

That's a Spicy Pizza!
Area of Circles

WARM UP

Determine a unit rate for each situation.

1. $38.40 for 16 gallons of gas

2. 15 miles jogged in 3.75 hours

3. $26.99 for 15 pounds

LEARNING GOALS

- Give an informal derivation of the relationship between the circumference and area of a circle and use the area formula to solve problems.
- Decide whether circumference or area is an appropriate measure for a problem situation.
- Calculate unit rates associated with circle areas.

KEY TERM

- unit rate

You have learned about the different parts and measures of a circle, including radius, diameter, and circumference. How can you use the parts of a circle to determine the area of a circle?

What Changed? What Stayed the Same?

The length of the base and height are the same in the parallelogram and rectangle shown.

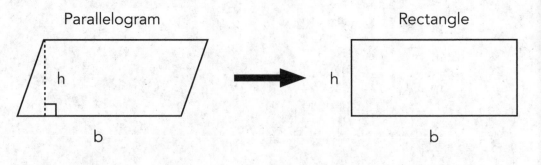

1. How could you rearrange the parallelogram to create the rectangle?

2. What is the area of each figure?

In the last lesson you derived formulas for the distance around a circle. In this lesson you will investigate the space within a circle. Use the circle at the end of the lesson that is divided into 4, 8, and 16 equal parts.

1. Follow the steps to decompose the circle and compose it into a new figure.

   a. First, cut the circle into fourths and arrange the parts side by side so that they form a shape that looks like a parallelogram.

   b. Then cut the circle into eighths and then sixteenths. Each time, arrange the parts to form a parallelogram.

2. Analyze the parallelogram you made each time.

   a. How did the parallelogram change as you arranged it with the smaller equal parts of the same circle?

   b. What would be the result if you built the parallelogram out of 40 equal circle sections? What about 100 equal circle sections?

   c. Represent the approximate base length and height of the parallelogram in terms of the radius and circumference of the circle.

d. Use your answers to part (c) to determine the formula for the area of the parallelogram.

e. How does the area of the parallelogram compare to the area of the circle?

f. Write a formula for the area of a circle.

3. Use different representations for π to calculate the area of a circle.

a. Calculate the area of each circle with the given radius. Round your answers to the nearest ten-thousandths, if necessary.

Value for π	$r = 6$ units	$r = 1.5$ units	$r = \frac{1}{2}$ units
π			
Use the π Key on a Calculator			
Use 3.14 for π			
Use $\frac{22}{7}$ for π			

b. Compare your area calculations for each circle. How do the different values of π affect your calculations?

4. Suppose the ratio of radius lengths of two circles is 1 unit to 2 units.

   a. What is the ratio of areas of the circles? Experiment with various radius lengths to make a conclusion.

   b. If the length of the radius of a circle is doubled, what effect will this have on the area?

Circumference or Area

Circle Formulas
$C = \pi d$, or $2\pi r$
$A = \pi r^2$

The circumference of a circle is the distance around the circle, while the area of a circle is the amount of space contained inside the circle. When solving problems involving circles, it is important to think about what you are trying to determine.

1. A city park has a large circular garden with a path around it. The diameter of the garden is 60 feet.

   a. Gina likes to walk along the circular path during her lunch breaks. How far does Gina walk if she completes one rotation around the path?

   b. Jason works for the City Park Department. He needs to spread plant food all over the garden. What is the area of the park he will cover with plant food?

2. Samantha is making a vegetable pizza. First, she presses the dough so that it fills a circular pan with a 16-inch diameter and covers it with sauce. What is the area of the pizza Samantha will cover with sauce?

3. Members of a community center have decided to paint a large circular mural in the middle of the parking lot. The radius of the mural is to be 11 yards. Before they begin painting the mural, they use rope to form the outline. How much rope will they need?

ACTIVITY
2.3
Unit Rates and Circle Area

Talarico's Pizza has a large variety of pizza sizes.

	Small	Medium	Large	X-Large	Enorme	Ginorme	Colossale
Diameter	10 in.	13 in.	16 in.	18 in.	24 in.	28 in.	36 in.
Slices	6	8	10	12	20	30	40
Cost	$6.99	$9.99	$12.99	$14.99	$22.99	$28.99	$54.99

Recall that a **unit rate** is a ratio of two different measures in which either the numerator or denominator is 1.

Lina and Michael are trying to decide whether to get two pizzas or one Ginorme pizza. They ask themselves, "Which choice is the better buy?"

They each calculated a unit rate for the Ginorme pizza.

Lina 👍

I Ginorme: $\dfrac{\pi(14)^2}{28.99} = \dfrac{196\pi}{28.99} \approx 21.24$ square inches per dollar

The Ginorme gives you approximately 21.24 square inches of pizza per dollar.

Michael

I Ginorme: $\dfrac{28.99}{14^2 \pi} = \dfrac{28.99}{196\pi} \approx \$0.05$ per square inch

The Ginorme costs approximately $0.05 for each square inch of pizza.

1. Consider Lina's and Michael's work.

   a. Explain why Lina's and Michael's unit rates are different but still both correct.

   b. How would you decide which pizza was the better buy if you calculated the unit rate for each pizza using Lina's method versus Michael's method.

2. Which of the seven sizes of pizza from Talarico's Pizza is the best buy? Explain your answer.

TALK the TALK

Go With the Flow

1. Which pipe configuration can deliver more water to residents, one 8-cm pipe or two 4-cm pipes? Show your work and explain your reasoning.

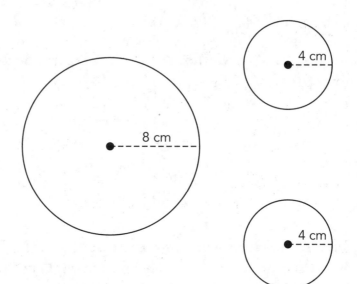

Circle Area Cutouts

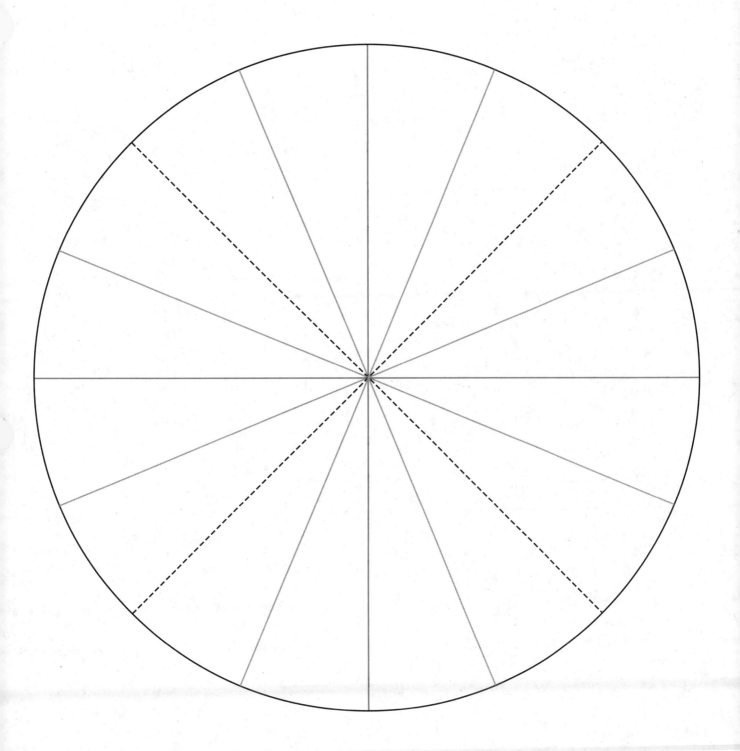

Assignment

Write

Explain in your own words how to derive the formula for the area of a circle.

Remember

A formula for the area of a circle is $A = \pi r^2$.

Practice

Determine the area of the circle, given each measurement. Use 3.14 for π and round to the nearest hundredth.

1. Diameter: 8 in.
2. Radius: 10 in.
3. Radius: 1.5 ft
4. Diameter: 8.8 yd
5. Diameter: $1\frac{3}{4}$ in.
6. Radius: $2\frac{1}{2}$ cm

Determine which pizza is the better buy in each situation.

7. The 10-inch diameter pizza for $8.99 or the 6-inch diameter pizza for $5.
8. The large 16-inch diameter pizza for $12.99 or the $26 X-large with a radius of 16 in.
9. The 12-inch diameter pizza for $12.50 or the 20-inch diameter pizza for $17.50.
10. The 4-inch radius pizza for $3 or the 8-inch radius pizza for $14.
11. Two 12-inch diameter pizzas for $12.98 or one large 14-inch diameter pizza for $7.99.
12. The 1-inch diameter pizza bite for $1 or the 10-inch diameter pizza for $10.

Stretch

The radius of the small circle is 0.5 millimeter. The area of the large circle is 28.26 square millimeters. Calculate the area of the shaded region.

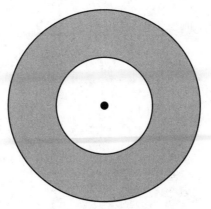

Review

Determine the circumference of each circle, given its radius or diameter. Use 3.14 for π and round to the nearest tenth.

1. Radius: 4.5 cm

2. Diameter: 12 ft

Determine each unit rate.

3. 75 square feet of tile for $126

4. 420 miles in 6.5 hours

Compare the fractions in each pair using the symbol $>$, $<$, or $=$.

5. $\dfrac{3}{5}, \dfrac{2}{3}$

6. $\dfrac{6}{7}, \dfrac{8}{9}$

Circular Reasoning

Solving Area and Circumference Problems

WARM UP

Determine the area of each circle. Use 3.14 for π.

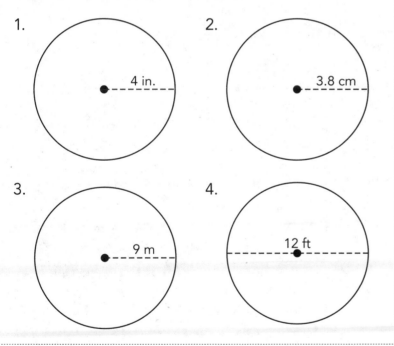

1.
4 in.

2.
3.8 cm

3.
9 m

4.
12 ft

LEARNING GOALS

- Use the area and circumference formulas for a circle to solve problems.
- Calculate the areas of composite figures.

You encounter circles regularly in life. Now that you know how to calculate the circumference and area of circles, what kind of problems can you solve?

A Winning Formula

Suppose that the circumference of a circle is approximately 157 centimeters.

1. Describe a strategy you can use to solve for the area of the circle.

When in doubt, use 3.14 for pi throughout this lesson.

2. Solve for the area of the circle. Use 3.14 for π.

ACTIVITY
3.1

A Maximum Area Problem

A friend gave you 120 feet of fencing. You decide to fence in a portion of the backyard for your dog. You want to maximize the amount of fenced land.

1. Draw a diagram, label the dimensions, and compute the maximum fenced area. Assume the fence is free-standing and you are not using any existing structure.

ACTIVITY 3.2 | **Composite Figure Problems**

A semicircle is half of a circle.

In previous grades you worked with composite figures made up of triangles and various quadrilaterals. Now that you know the area of a circle, you can calculate the area of more interesting composite figures.

1. **A figure is composed of a rectangle and two semicircles. Determine the area of the figure.**

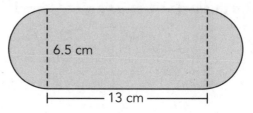

6.5 cm

13 cm

2. **A figure is composed of a trapezoid and a semicircle. Determine the area of the figure.**

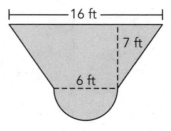

16 ft

7 ft

6 ft

3. **A figure is composed of a triangle and three semicircles. Determine the area of the figure.**

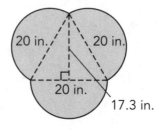

20 in.   20 in.

20 in.

17.3 in.

Shaded Region Problems

You have worked with composite figures by adding on areas. Now let's think about subtracting areas.

1. In the concentric circles shown, *R* represents the radius of the larger circle and *r* represents the radius of the smaller circle. Suppose that $R = 8$ centimeters and $r = 3$ centimeters. Calculate the area of the shaded region.

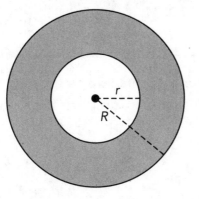

Concentric circles are circles with a common center. The region bounded by two concentric circles is called the **annulus**.

2. A circle is inscribed in a square. Determine the area of the shaded region.

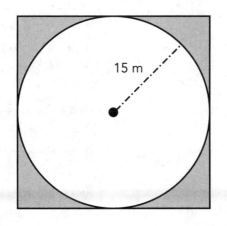

15 m

When a circle is inscribed in a square, the diameter of the circle is equal to the side length of the square.

3. Two small circles are drawn that touch each other, and both circles touch the large circle. Determine the area of the shaded region.

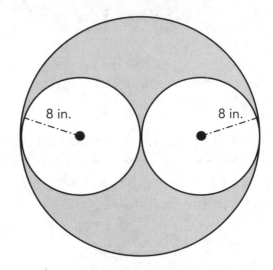

8 in.

8 in.

4. Jimmy and Matthew each said the area of the shaded region is about 402 square inches. Compare their strategies.

Jimmy 👍

Area of 1 small circle
$A \approx 3.14(8)^2$
$A \approx 3.14(64)$
$A \approx 200.96$

Area of 2 small circles
$A \approx 2(200.96)$
$A \approx 401.92$

Area of large circle
$A \approx (3.14)(16)^2$
$A \approx (3.14)(256)$
$A \approx 803.84$

Area of shaded region
$803.84 - 401.92 \approx 401.92$

The area of the shaded region is about 402 sq in.

Matthew 👍

Area of 1 small circle
$A = \pi(8)^2$
$A = 64\pi$

Area of 2 small circles
$A = 2(64\pi)$
$A = 128\pi$

Area of large circle
$A = \pi(16)^2$
$A = 256\pi$

Area of shaded region
$256\pi - 128\pi = 128\pi$
$A = 128\pi$
$A \approx 402.12$

This means the area of the shaded region is about 402 sq in.

a. What did Jimmy and Matthew do the same?

b. What was different about their strategies?

c. Which strategy do you prefer?

5. Determine the area of each shaded region.

a. One medium circle and one small circle touch each other,
and each circle touches the large circle.

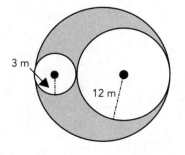
3 m
12 m

b. A rectangle is inscribed in a circle.

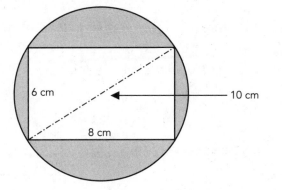
6 cm
10 cm
8 cm

A rectangle is
inscribed in a
circle when all the
vertices of the
rectangle touch the
circumference of
the circle.

c. A circle is inside a regular hexagon.

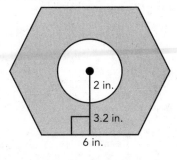
2 in.
3.2 in.
6 in.

TALK the TALK

Rupert's Leash

Jamal loves his dog, Rupert. On sunny days, Jamal keeps Rupert on a 12-foot leash in the backyard. The leash is secured to a stake in the ground.

1. Determine the diameter, circumference, and area of Rupert's play area. Use 3.14 for π.

2. Suppose Jamal wants to give Rupert a little more room to play. He uses a 15-foot leash instead of the 12-foot leash. What is the area of Rupert's play area now? Use 3.14 for π.

Assignment

Write

Write the area and circumference formulas for circles.

Describe pi in terms of the area and radius of a circle. Describe pi in terms of the circumference and radius of a circle.

Remember

Given a specific length to form a perimeter or circumference, arranging that length into the shape of a circle provides the maximum area.

Practice

Calculate the area of the shaded region in each figure. Use 3.14 for π and round to the nearest tenth, if necessary.

1.

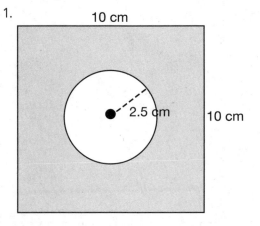

2.

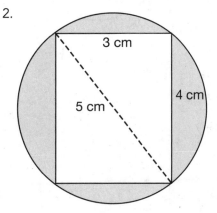

3.

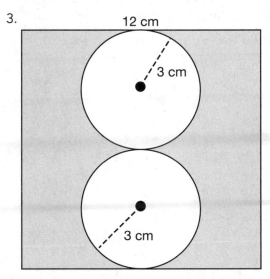

4.

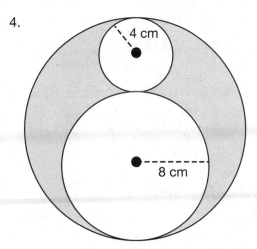

Stretch

1. Determine the area of the shaded region. All circles have the same radius of 10 inches.

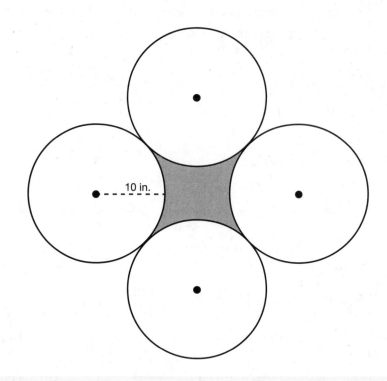

10 in.

Review

Solve each problem.

1. Jose is adding mulch to an existing round flower bed. The length of the rubber edging around the flower bed is 25.12 feet. What is the area that Jose needs to cover with mulch?

2. Nami is adding a mosaic pattern to the top of a small round table. The distance around the edge of the table top is 4.7 feet. What is the area that Nami needs to cover with the mosaic pattern?

Determine each area.

3. Area of a triangle with a base length of 4 in. and a height of 9 in.

4. Area of a parallelogram with a base length of 2.9 ft and a height of 5.5 ft.

5. Area of a trapezoid with a top base length of 6 cm, a bottom base length of 12 cm, and a height of 5 cm.

Write a unit rate for each ratio.

6. $\dfrac{28 \text{ cm}}{4 \text{ square feet}}$

7. $\dfrac{5.15 \text{ yd}}{5 \text{ square feet}}$

Circles and Ratio Summary

KEY TERMS

- congruent
- circle
- radius

- diameter
- circumference

- pi
- unit rate

LESSON 1

Pi: The Ultimate Ratio

A **circle** is a collection of points on the same plane equidistant from the same point. The center of a circle is the point from which all points on the circle are equidistant.

A **radius** of a circle is a line segment formed by connecting a point on the circle and the center of the circle. The distance across a circle through the center is a **diameter** of the circle. A diameter of a circle is a line segment formed by connecting two points on the circle such that the line segment passes through the center point.

Circles are named by their center point. For example, the circle shown is Circle B. A radius of Circle B is line segment FB. A diameter of Circle B is line segment AH.

The distance around a circle is called the **circumference** of the circle. The number **pi** (π) is the ratio of the circumference of a circle to its diameter. That is, $\text{pi} = \dfrac{\text{circumference of a circle}}{\text{diameter of a circle}}$, or $\pi = \dfrac{C}{d}$, where C is the circumference of the circle, and d is the diameter of the circle. The number π has an infinite number of decimal digits that never repeat. Some approximations used for the value π are 3.14 and $\dfrac{22}{7}$. You can use the ratio to write a formula for the circumference of a circle: $C = \pi d$.

Congruent means that it has the same shape and size. For example, Circle *X* is congruent to Circle *B*. If line segment *AH* on Circle *B* has a length of 10 centimeters, then the circumference of Circle *X* is $C = \pi(10)$ centimeters, or approximately 31.4 centimeters.

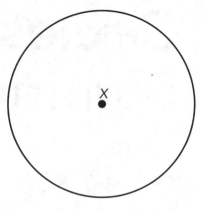

That's a Spicy Pizza!

The circumference of a circle is the distance around the circle, while the area of a circle is the amount of space contained inside the circle. The formula for the area of a circle is $A = \pi r^2$.

The area formula for a circle can be derived by dividing a circle into a large number of equal-sized wedges. Laying these wedges as shown, you can see that they will form an approximate rectangle with a length of πr and a height of r.

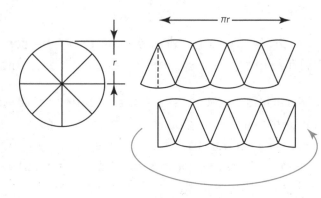

A **unit rate** is a ratio of two different measures in which either the numerator or denominator is 1.

For example, a large pizza with a diameter of 18 inches costs \$14.99. The rate of area to cost is $\frac{\pi \cdot 9^2}{14.99} = \frac{81\pi}{14.99}$. Using 3.14 for π, the unit rate is approximately 16.97 square inches per dollar. The unit rate of cost to area is $\frac{1}{16.97}$, or approximately \$0.06 per square inch.

Circular Reasoning

Given a specific length to form a perimeter or circumference, arranging that length into the shape of a circle provides the maximum area.

For example, suppose you have 176 feet of fencing to use to fence off a portion of your backyard for planting vegetables. You want to maximize the amount of fenced land. Calculate the maximum fenced area you will have.

The length of fencing you have will form the circumference of a circle. Use the formula for the circumference of a circle to determine the diameter of the fenced area.

$$C = \pi d$$
$$176 = \pi d$$
$$56 \approx d$$

If the diameter of the fenced area is about 56 feet, the radius is 28 feet. Use this information to calculate the area of the fenced land.

$$A = \pi r^2$$
$$A = \pi \cdot 28^2$$

The maximum fenced area you will have is about 2461.76 square feet.

$$A = 784\pi \approx 2461.76$$

Many geometric figures are composed of two or more geometric shapes. These figures are known as composite figures. When solving problems involving composite figures, it is often necessary to calculate the area of each figure and then add these areas together.

For example, a figure is composed of a rectangle and two semi-circles. Determine the area of the figure.

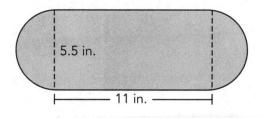

5.5 in.

11 in.

Calculate the area of the rectangle.

$$A = l \times w$$
$$A = (11)(5.5)$$
$$A = 60.5 \text{ square inches}$$

The two semi-circles together make one circle. Calculate the area of the circle.

$$A = \pi r^2$$
$$A = \pi(2.75)^2$$
$$A = 7.5625\pi \approx 23.75 \text{ square inches}$$

The area of the composite figure is approximately 60.5 square inches plus 23.75 square inches, or 84.55 square inches.

When determining the area of a shaded region of a figure, it is often necessary to calculate the area of a figure and subtract it from the area of a second figure.

For example, this figure shows a circle inscribed in a square. Determine the area of the shaded region.

When a circle is inscribed in a square, the diameter of the circle is equal to the side length of the square.

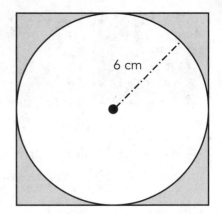

6 cm

Calculate the area of the square.

$A = s^2$

$A = 12^2$

$A = 144$ square centimeters

Calculate the area of the circle.

$A = \pi r^2$

$A = \pi(6)^2$

$A = 36\pi \approx 113.04$ square inches

The area of the shaded region is approximately 144 square centimeters minus 113.04 square centimeters, or 30.96 square centimeters.

TOPIC 2
Fractional Rates

The brain-to-body mass ratio for an elephant is 1:560. For a human it's 1:50.

Lesson 1
Making Punch

Unit Rate Representations M1-51

Lesson 2
Eggzactly!

Solving Problems with Ratios of Fractions M1-59

Lesson 3
Tagging Sharks

Solving Proportions Using Means and Extremes M1-69

Module 1: Thinking Proportionally

TOPIC 2: FRACTIONAL RATES

In this topic, students extend their work with rates to include rates with fractional values. To begin the topic, students write, analyze, and use unit rates with whole numbers and fractions to solve problems. Next, students calculate and use unit rates from ratios of fractions. Finally, students review strategies for solving problems involving equivalent ratios and proportions.

Where have we been?

In grade 6, students learned about ratios, rates, unit rates, and proportions, and they represented ratios and unit rates with tables and graphs. Students used a variety of informal strategies to compare ratios and to determine equivalent ratios and solve simple proportions (e.g., double number lines, scaling up and down, conversion factors).

Where are we going?

This topic broadens students' range of numbers and strategies for solving ratio and proportion problems, preparing them to dig deeper into representations of proportional relationships in the next topic and solving multistep ratio and percent problems in future lessons.

Using Means and Extremes to Solve Proportions

In the proportion $\frac{a}{b} = \frac{c}{d}$, the terms b and c are called the means, and the terms a and d are called the extremes.

$$\text{extremes}$$
$$3 : 4 = 9 : 12 \qquad \text{or}$$
$$\text{means}$$
$$(4)(9) = (3)(12)$$

$$\frac{3}{4} \underset{\times}{=} \frac{9}{12}$$
$$\text{means} \quad \text{extremes}$$
$$(4)(9) = (3)(12)$$

Myth: "If I can get the right answer, then I should not have to explain why."

Sometimes you get the right answer for the wrong reasons. Suppose a student is asked, "What is 4 divided by 2?" and she confidently answers "2!" If she does not explain any further, then it might be assumed that she understands how to divide whole numbers. But, what if she used the following rule to solve that problem? "Subtract 2 from 4 one time." Even though she gave the right answer, she has an incomplete understanding of division.

However, if she is asked to explain her reasoning, either by drawing a picture, creating a model, or giving a different example, the teacher has a chance to remediate her flawed understanding. If teachers aren't exposed to their students' reasoning for both right and wrong answers, then they won't know about or be able to address misconceptions. This is important because mathematics is cumulative in the sense that new lessons build upon previous understandings.

You should ask your student to explain his or her thinking, when possible, even if you don't know whether the explanation is correct. When children (and adults!) explain something to someone else, it helps them learn. Just the process of trying to explain is helpful.

#mathmythbusted

Talking Points

You can further support your student's learning by asking questions about the work they do in class or at home. Your student is learning to reason using fractional rates.

Questions to Ask

- How does this problem look like something you did in class?
- Can you show me the strategy you used to solve this problem? Do you know another way to solve it?
- Does your answer make sense? How do you know?

Key Terms

complex ratio
A complex ratio is a ratio in which the numerator, denominator, or both are fractions.

isolate the variable
When you isolate the variable in an equation, you perform an operation, or operations, to get the variable by itself on one side of the equals sign.

inverse operations
Inverse operations are operations that "undo" each other. Multiplication and division are inverse operations.

Making Punch

Unit Rate Representations

WARM UP

Determine a unit rate in terms of each quantity for the given ratio.

1. 24 bracelets : 6 hours

2. 153 miles : 9 gallons

3. $48 : 3 pounds

4. 45 students : 3 teachers

LEARNING GOALS

- Compute unit rates associated with ratios of whole numbers and fractions.
- Represent unit rates using tables and graphs.
- Use unit rates to solve problems.

You have learned about ratios, rates, and unit rates. How can you use tables and graphs to represent unit rates and solve problems?

The Pumpkin-iest!

Paige loves everything pumpkin: pumpkin waffles, pumpkin hand soap, pumpkin chili . . . Now she's trying to make the perfect pumpkin smoothie. She is using this recipe:

Pumpkin Smoothie Recipe	
• 1 banana ($\frac{3}{4}$ cup)	• $\frac{1}{4}$ teaspoon pumpkin pie spice
• $\frac{1}{4}$ teaspoon cinnamon	• 1 cup ice
• 2 tablespoons maple syrup	• $\frac{2}{3}$ cup pumpkin puree
• $\frac{1}{2}$ cup milk	• $\frac{1}{2}$ cup vanilla yogurt

Paige wants to experiment with the given recipe.

1. What ingredients can Paige increase to make the smoothie more pumpkin-y? Less pumpkin-y?

2. What ingredients can Paige decrease to make the smoothie more pumpkin-y? Less pumpkin-y?

Determining Unit Rates

Four students share their recipes for lemon-lime punch. The class decides to analyze the recipes to determine which one will make the fruitiest tasting punch.

Mason's Recipe	Tyler's Recipe
4 cups lemon-lime concentrate 8 cups club soda	3 cups lemon-lime concentrate 5 cups club soda
Carlos's Recipe	Zeb's Recipe
2 cups lemon-lime concentrate 3 cups club soda	1 cup lemon-lime concentrate 4 cups club soda

1. Which recipe has the strongest taste of lemon-lime?
   Show your work and explain your reasoning.

2. Which has the weakest taste of lemon-lime? Show your work
   and explain your reasoning.

Emily and Julio each used unit rates to compare Mason's and Tyler's recipes.

Emily

Mason's recipe
4 cups lemon-lime : 8 cups club soda
The unit rate is $\frac{1}{2}$ cup lemon-lime per 1 cup of club soda

Tyler's recipe
3 cups lemon-lime : 5 cups club soda
The unit rate is $\frac{3}{5}$ cup lemon-lime per 1 cup of club soda

$\frac{3}{5} > \frac{1}{2}$, so Tyler's recipe has the stronger taste of lemon-lime.

Julio

Mason's recipe
4 cups lemon-lime : 12 cups total punch
The unit rate is $\frac{1}{3}$ cup lemon-lime per cup of punch

Tyler's recipe
3 cups lemon-lime : 8 cups total punch
The unit rate is $\frac{3}{8}$ cup lemon-lime per cup of punch

$\frac{3}{8} > \frac{1}{3}$, so Tyler's recipe has the stronger taste of lemon-lime.

3. Compare Julio's and Emily's strategies. In what ways are they different? How did they arrive at the same answer?

4. Complete each table and include the unit rate of lemon-lime for each cup of punch for each recipe. Then draw a graph for each recipe on the coordinate plane. Label each graph with the person's recipe and the unit rate.

Mason's Recipe				
Lemon-Lime (c)				
Total Punch (c)	1			

Tyler's Recipe				
Lemon-Lime (c)				
Total Punch (c)	1			

Carlos's Recipe				
Lemon-Lime (c)				
Total Punch (c)	1			

Zeb's Recipe				
Lemon-Lime (c)				
Total Punch (c)	1			

The steepness of a graphed line is called its slope.

5. What does the steepness of each line represent?

6. How could you use the graphs to determine which recipe has the strongest lemon-lime taste?

TALK the TALK

Getting Unit Rate-ier

Look back at the activity *The Pumpkin-iest!* Use the smoothie recipe to answer each question.

1. One teaspoon is approximately $\frac{1}{50}$ cup, and 1 tablespoon is equal to 3 teaspoons. Approximately how many cups of smoothie does Paige's recipe make?

2. How pumpkin-y are Paige's smoothies if she follows the recipe? Write a unit rate to represent the amount of pumpkin-y ingredients per cup of smoothie.

Assignment

Write

How can unit rates be helpful when solving problems?

Remember

A rate is a ratio that compares quantities with different units. A unit rate is a rate in which the numerator or denominator (or both) is 1.

A unit rate is represented by the ordered pair (1, *r*) on a coordinate plane.

Practice

Complete each table and write a unit rate for the given situation.

1. General house cleaning (sweeping the floors, vacuuming, laundry, etc.) can burn 470 calories every 2 hours.

Time (hours)	1	2	3	4	5
Calories burned					

2. A full strip plus another half of a strip of staples contains 315 staples.

Number of Strips	$\frac{1}{2}$	1	$1\frac{1}{2}$	2	$2\frac{1}{2}$
Number of Staples					

3. Victoria is making punch for a school party. The recipe she is using calls for 2 cups of lemonade to make 5 cups of punch.

Cups of Lemonade					
Cups of Punch					

Complete each table and write a unit rate for the given situation. Then, graph the relationship on a coordinate plane.

4. The owner of a city parking garage uses a rate table so that he can look up the parking charges quickly.

Hours	$\frac{1}{2}$	1	$1\frac{1}{2}$	2	$2\frac{1}{2}$	3	$3\frac{1}{2}$	4
Charge	$2.25							

5. The owner of a city parking garage uses a rate table so that he can look up the parking charges quickly.

Hours	$\frac{1}{2}$	1	$1\frac{1}{2}$	2	$2\frac{1}{2}$	3	$3\frac{1}{2}$	4
Charge				$13.00				

Stretch

A line is graphed through points at (4, 5) and (8 10). What is the ordered pair of the unit rate?

Review

Use the circle shown to answer each question. Use 3.14 for π. Round to the nearest hundredth.

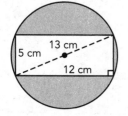

1. Calculate the exact area of the circle.
2. Calculate the circumference of the circle.
3. Determine the total area of the shaded regions.

Use 3.14 for π. Round to the nearest hundredth.
4. Ben's dog, Tripp, is on a leash that is 6 feet long. What is the approximate circular area of Tripp's play area?

Determine each number.
5. 49 is 70% of what number?
6. 99 is 36% of what number?

Eggzactly!

Solving Problems with Ratios of Fractions

WARM UP

Determine each product or quotient.

1. $\frac{1}{2} \times \frac{3}{5}$

2. $\frac{5}{8} \times \frac{8}{5}$

3. $\frac{2}{3} \div \frac{3}{8}$

4. $\frac{3}{4} \div 1\frac{1}{2}$

LEARNING GOALS

- Compute unit rates from ratios of fractions, including ratios of lengths and areas.
- Interpret complex rates to solve real-world problems involving lengths and areas.

KEY TERM

- complex ratio

You have learned about rates and unit rates. You have written unit rates from ratios of whole numbers. How can you write ratios of fractions as unit rates in order to solve problems?

A Different Form, But Still the Same

Ratios can be written using any numbers. A ratio in which one or both of the quantities being compared are written as fractions is called a **complex ratio**.

For example, traveling $\frac{1}{3}$ mile in $\frac{1}{2}$ hour represents a ratio of fractions, or a complex ratio. It is also an example of a rate, since the units being compared are different.

You can write this ratio in fractional form: $\frac{\frac{1}{3}}{\frac{1}{2}}$.

1. Rewrite each given rate as an equivalent ratio of fractions, or complex ratio, by converting one or both units of measure.

   a. One half-inch of rain fell in fifteen minutes.

   b. Sam ran 3520 feet in 20 minutes.

   c. The baby gained 6 ounces every week.

   d. Gas costs $2.50 per gallon.

Think about equivalent relationships. Fifteen minutes is what fraction of an hour?

Comparing Ratios of Fractions

The table shows the weights of four different adult birds and the weights of their eggs.

	Mother's Weight (oz)	Egg Weight (oz)
Pigeon	10	$\frac{3}{4}$
Chicken	80	2
Swan	352	11
Robin	$2\frac{1}{2}$	$\frac{1}{10}$

1. Compare the weights of the eggs. List the birds in order from the bird with the heaviest egg to the bird with the lightest egg.

2. Determine the ratio of egg weight to mother's weight for each bird.

3. Compare the ratios of egg weight to mother's weight. List the birds in order from greatest to least ratio.

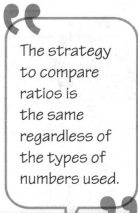

The strategy to compare ratios is the same regardless of the types of numbers used.

Although the ostrich is the largest living bird, it is also the fastest runner. The table shows distances that four birds ran, and the amount of time it took each bird to run that distance.

Bird	Distance Covered	Time
Ostrich	22 miles	$\frac{1}{2}$ hour
Greater Roadrunner	300 yards	$\frac{1}{2}$ minute
Quail	20 yards	$2\frac{1}{2}$ seconds
Pheasant	200 yards	$\frac{5}{6}$ minute

Remember, a rate is a ratio that compares two quantities that are measured in different units.

Each row in the table shows a rate. The rate for each bird in this situation is the distance covered per the amount of time.

1. Write the rate for each bird as a complex rate.

   a. Ostrich

   b. Greater Roadrunner

   c. Quail

   d. Pheasant

The rates you wrote in Question 1 are each represented using different units of measure. In order to compare speeds let's determine the unit rate in miles per hour for each bird. Consider the numbers and units of the original rate to choose a strategy. Analyze each worked example.

You know that the ostrich ran 22 miles in $\frac{1}{2}$ hour.

WORKED EXAMPLE

The rate of the ostrich is already measured in miles and hours. You can set up a proportion and scale the original rate up to 1 hour.

$$\text{distance} \longrightarrow \overset{\times 2}{\overbrace{\frac{22 \text{ mi}}{\frac{1}{2} \text{ h}}}} = \underset{\times 2}{\underbrace{\frac{44 \text{ mi}}{1 \text{ h}}}}$$

$$= \frac{44 \text{ mi}}{1 \text{ h}}$$

The ostrich's speed is 44 miles per hour.

---

2. **Why was the scale factor of 2 used in this worked example?**

There are 1760 yards in 1 mile.

You know that the Greater Roadrunner ran 300 yards in $\frac{1}{2}$ minute.

WORKED EXAMPLE

The rate of the Greater Roadrunner is written in yards per minute. You can use conversion rates to rewrite the rate in miles per hour.

$$\frac{300 \text{ yd}}{\frac{1}{2} \text{ min}} \cdot \frac{60 \text{ min}}{1 \text{ hr}} \cdot \frac{1 \text{ mi}}{1760 \text{ yd}}$$

$$\frac{300 \text{ y\!d}}{\frac{1}{2} \text{ m\!in}} \cdot \frac{60 \text{ m\!in}}{1 \text{ hr}} \cdot \frac{1 \text{ mi}}{1760 \text{ y\!d}}$$

$$\frac{300}{\frac{1}{2}} \cdot \frac{60}{1} \cdot \frac{1}{1760} \frac{\text{mi}}{\text{hr}}$$

$$600 \cdot 60 \cdot \frac{1}{1760} \frac{\text{mi}}{\text{hr}} \approx \frac{20.5 \text{ mi}}{1 \text{ hr}}$$

---

3. Why is the fractional representation of each conversion rate important?

4. Determine the quail's and pheasant's speeds in miles per hour.

   a. quail's speed:

   b. pheasant's speed:

5. Write the birds in order from the fastest rate to the slowest rate.

1. Tony needs a rate table for his tutoring jobs so that he can look up the charge quickly.

   a. Complete the rate table.

Time (Hours)	$\frac{1}{2}$	1	$1\frac{1}{2}$	2	3	$3\frac{1}{2}$	4
Charge ($)			37.50				

   b. How much would Tony charge for $7\frac{1}{2}$ hours of tutoring?

   c. Tony made $212.50 last weekend. How long did he tutor? Explain how you solved the problem.

2. At Pepe's Pizzas, a new deal gives you $1\frac{1}{2}$ orders of wings for half the price of a single order. Without the deal, a single order of wings costs $12. What is the cost of a single order of wings with the deal?

3. Abby uses $3\frac{3}{4}$ scoops of drink mix to make 10 cups of drinks.

   a. How much drink mix would she need to use to make 1 cup of drink?

   b. She only has $11\frac{1}{4}$ scoops of drink mix remaining. How many cups of drink can she make?

4. The square shown is composed of smaller equally-sized squares. The shaded section has an area of $\frac{9}{25}$ square inches. What is the area of the large square?

TALK the TALK

True, False, Example

Determine whether each statement is true or false. Provide one or more examples and an explanation to justify your answer.

1. To compute a unit rate associated with a ratio of fractions, multiply both the numerator and denominator by the reciprocal of the denominator.   True   False

2. Any ratio can be written as a complex ratio.   True   False

3. You never scale down to write a complex rate as a unit rate.   True   False

4. A statement with the word "per" is always a unit rate.   True   False

5. Dividing the numerator by the denominator is one way to convert a rate to a unit rate.   True   False

Assignment

Write

Write a definition for *complex ratio*, provide an example, and show how your example can be converted into a unit rate.

Remember

To convert a complex rate to a unit rate, you can multiply the numerator and denominator by the reciprocal of the denominator, or you can use the definition of division.

$$\frac{\frac{1}{2}}{\frac{1}{4}} \times \frac{\frac{4}{1}}{\frac{4}{1}} = \frac{\frac{4}{2}}{1}$$

$$= 2$$

$$\frac{\frac{1}{2}}{\frac{1}{4}} = \frac{1}{2} \div \frac{1}{4}$$

$$= \frac{1}{2} \cdot 4 = 2$$

Practice

1. The table shows the gallons filled in a pool over time.

Number of Hours	$\frac{1}{4}$	$\frac{3}{4}$	$1\frac{1}{2}$	$2\frac{1}{2}$
Gallons Filled		$637\frac{1}{2}$		

   a. Complete the table.

   b. Determine a unit rate for this situation.

   c. Use a unit rate to calculate the gallons filled in 5.5 hours.

   d. Use a unit rate to determine about how many minutes it will take to fill 100 gallons in the pool.

2. The rectangle shown is composed of smaller equally-sized squares. The shaded section has an area of $\frac{3}{16}$ square inches. Use a unit rate to determine the area of the larger rectangle.

Stretch

An HOn2-scale train is a model train that is constructed at the ratio 1 : 87.1. If an HOn2 model of a locomotive is 10.4712 inches long, how long is the actual locomotive in feet?

Review

Determine each unit rate and graph each rate on the coordinate plane.

1. $\frac{3}{4}$ cup of punch to $\frac{1}{8}$ cup of lemon-lime

2. 1 cup of lemon-lime : $1\frac{1}{2}$ cups of punch

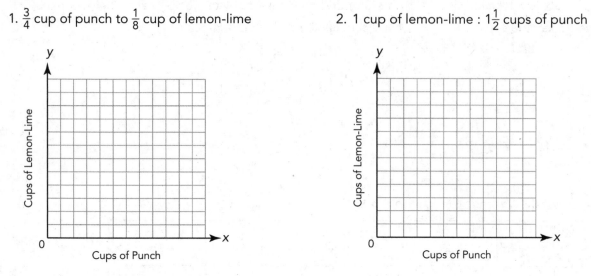

Answer each question. Use 3.14 for π. Round to the nearest hundredth.

3. The diameter of a circle is 4 cm. Determine the area of the circle.

4. The radius of a circle is 5.24 ft. Determine the circumference of the circle.

Determine each sum or product.

5. 71.05 + 0.54

6. 89.2 × 5.3

Tagging Sharks

3

Solving Proportions Using Means and Extremes

WARM UP

Solve each equation.

1. $w - 5 = 25$
2. $9x = 990$
3. $\frac{c}{12} = 48$
4. $1.15 + m = 10$

LEARNING GOALS

- Rewrite proportions to maintain equality.
- Represent proportional relationships by equations.
- Develop strategies to solve proportions.
- Use proportional relationships to solve multistep problems.

KEY TERMS

- proportion
- variable
- means
- extremes
- solve a proportion
- isolate the variable
- inverse operations

You have learned how to write proportions and calculate unknown values through scaling up and scaling down. Is there a more efficient strategy that works for any unknown in any proportion?

Mix-N-Match

Recall that a **proportion** is an equation that states that two ratios are equal.

A proportion can be written several ways. Each example shows three proportions using the same four quantities.

	Example 1	Example 2
Proportion 1	$\frac{2}{3} = \frac{4}{6}$	$\frac{5}{7} = \frac{15}{21}$
Proportion 2	$\frac{6}{3} = \frac{4}{2}$	$\frac{21}{7} = \frac{15}{5}$
Proportion 3	$\frac{2}{4} = \frac{3}{6}$	$\frac{5}{15} = \frac{7}{21}$

1. In each example, use arrows to show how the numbers were rearranged from the:

   a. first proportion to the second proportion.

   b. first proportion to the third proportion.

Maintaining Equality with Proportions

Because it is impossible to count each individual animal, marine biologists use a method called the capture-recapture method to estimate the population of certain sea creatures. In certain areas of the world, biologists randomly catch and tag a given number of sharks. After a period of time, such as a month, they recapture a second sample of sharks and count the total number of sharks as well as the number of recaptured tagged sharks. Then, the biologists use proportions to estimate the population of sharks living in a certain area.

Biologists can set up a proportion to estimate the total number of sharks in an area.

$$\frac{\text{Original number of tagged sharks}}{\text{Total number of sharks in an area}} = \frac{\text{Number of recaptured tagged sharks}}{\text{Number of sharks caught in the second sample}}$$

Although capturing the sharks once is necessary for tagging, it is not necessary to recapture the sharks each time. At times, the tags can be observed through binoculars from a boat or at shore.

Biologists originally caught and tagged 24 sharks off the coast of Cape Cod, Massachusetts, and then released them back into the bay. The next month, they caught 80 sharks with 8 of the sharks already tagged. To estimate the shark population off the Cape Cod coast, biologists set up the following proportion:

$$\frac{24 \text{ tagged sharks}}{p \text{ total sharks}} = \frac{8 \text{ recaptured tagged sharks}}{80 \text{ total sharks}}$$

Notice the variable p in the proportion. In this proportion, let p represent the total shark population off the coast of Cape Cod.

A **variable** is a letter or symbol used to represent a number.

1. Write three additional different proportions you could use to determine the total shark population off the coast of Cape Cod.

2. Estimate the total shark population using any of the proportions.

3. Did any of the proportions seem more efficient than the other proportions?

4. Wildlife biologists tag deer in wildlife refuges. They originally tagged 240 deer and released them back into the refuge. The next month, they observed 180 deer, of which 30 deer were tagged. Approximately how many deer are in the refuge? Write a proportion and show your work to determine your answer.

A proportion of the form $\frac{a}{b} = \frac{c}{d}$ can be written in many different ways.

Another example is $\frac{d}{b} = \frac{c}{a}$ or $\frac{c}{a} = \frac{d}{b}$.

5. Show how the variables were rearranged from the proportion in the "if" statement to each proportion in the "then" statement to maintain equality.

If $\frac{a}{b} = \frac{c}{d}$, then $\frac{d}{b} = \frac{c}{a}$.

If $\frac{d}{b} = \frac{c}{a}$, then $\frac{c}{a} = \frac{d}{b}$.

6. Write all the different ways you can rewrite the proportion $\frac{a}{b} = \frac{c}{d}$ and maintain equality.

ACTIVITY 3.2

Solving Proportions with Means and Extremes

The Ready Steady Battery Company tests batteries as they come through the assembly line and then uses a proportion to predict how many of its total production might be defective.

On Friday, the quality controller tested every tenth battery and found that of the 320 batteries tested, 8 were defective. If the company shipped a total of 3200 batteries, how many might be defective?

A quality control department checks the product a company creates to ensure that the product is not defective.

Let's analyze a few methods.

John David

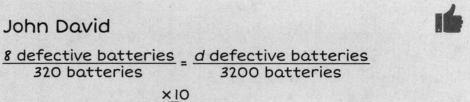

$$\frac{8 \text{ defective batteries}}{320 \text{ batteries}} = \frac{d \text{ defective batteries}}{3200 \text{ batteries}}$$

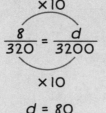

$$\frac{8}{320} = \frac{d}{3200}$$

×10

×10

$$d = 80$$

So, 80 batteries might be defective.

Parker

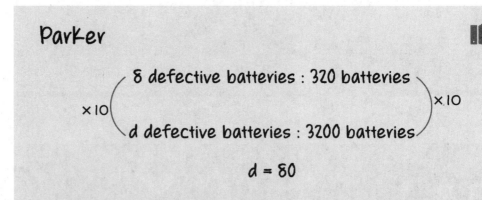

×10 8 defective batteries : 320 batteries ×10

d defective batteries : 3200 batteries

$$d = 80$$

About 80 batteries will probably be defective.

1. How are Parker's and John David's methods similar?

Nora

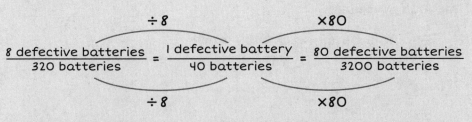

"One out of every 40 batteries is defective. So, out of 3200 batteries, 80 batteries could be defective because 3200 ÷ 40 = 80."

2. Describe the strategy Nora used.

Natalie

When I write Nora's ratios using colons like Parker, I notice something about proportions . . .

8 : 320 = 1 : 40

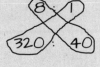

1 : 40 = 80 : 3200

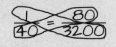

. . . the two middle numbers have the same product as the two outside numbers. So, I can solve any proportion by setting these two products equal to each other.

3. Verify that Natalie is correct.

4. Try the various proportion-solving methods on these proportions and determine the unknown value. Explain which method you used.

a. $\dfrac{3 \text{ granola bars}}{420 \text{ calories}} = \dfrac{g \text{ granola bars}}{140 \text{ calories}}$

b. 8 correct : 15 questions = 24 correct : q questions

c. $\dfrac{d \text{ dollars}}{5 \text{ miles}} = \dfrac{\$9}{7.5 \text{ miles}}$

> Multiplying the means and extremes is like "cross-multiplying."

The relationship that Natalie noticed is between the *means* and *extremes*. In a proportion that is written a : b = c : d, the product of the two values in the middle (the **means**) equals the product of the two values on the outside (the **extremes**).

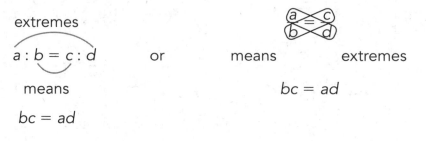

extremes

$a : b = c : d$ or   means   extremes

means

$bc = ad$ $bc = ad$

when $b \neq 0$, $d \neq 0$

To solve a proportion using this method, first, identify the means and extremes. Then, set the product of the means equal to the product of the extremes and solve for the unknown quantity. To **solve a proportion** means to determine all the values of the variables that make the proportion true.

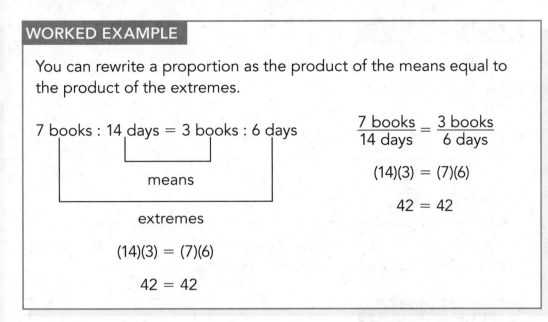

You can rewrite a proportion as the product of the means equal to the product of the extremes.

7 books : 14 days = 3 books : 6 days

means

extremes

$(14)(3) = (7)(6)$

$42 = 42$

$$\frac{7 \text{ books}}{14 \text{ days}} = \frac{3 \text{ books}}{6 \text{ days}}$$

$(14)(3) = (7)(6)$

$42 = 42$

5. You can rewrite the product of the means and extremes from the worked example as four different equations. Analyze each equation.

$$3 = \frac{(7)(6)}{14} \qquad 14 = \frac{(7)(6)}{3} \qquad \frac{(3)(14)}{7} = 6 \qquad \frac{(3)(14)}{6} = 7$$

a. Why are these equations all true? Explain your reasoning.

b. Compare these equations to the equation showing the product of the means equal to the product of the extremes. How was the balance of the equation maintained in each?

6. Why is it important to maintain balance in equations?

In the proportion $\frac{a}{b} = \frac{c}{d}$, you can multiply both sides by b to *isolate the variable a*.

$$b \cdot \frac{a}{b} = b \cdot \frac{c}{d} \longrightarrow a = \frac{bc}{d}$$

When you **isolate the variable** in an equation, you perform an operation, or operations, to get the variable by itself on one side of the equals sign. Multiplication and division are *inverse operations*. **Inverse operations** are operations that "undo" each other.

WORKED EXAMPLE

Another strategy to isolate the variable a is to multiply the means and extremes and then isolate the variable by performing inverse operations.

$$\frac{a}{b} = \frac{c}{d}$$

Step 1: $\qquad ad = bc$

Step 2: $\qquad \dfrac{ad}{d} = \dfrac{bc}{d}$

Step 3: $\qquad a = \dfrac{bc}{d}$

7. Describe each step shown.

8. Rewrite the proportion $\frac{a}{b} = \frac{c}{d}$ to isolate each of the other variables: b, c, and d. Explain the strategies you used to isolate each variable.

Solving Problems with Proportions

Write and solve proportions to solve each problem.

1. An astronaut who weighs 85 kilograms on Earth weighs 14.2 kilograms on the Moon. How much would a person weigh on the Moon if they weigh 95 kilograms on Earth? Round your answer to the nearest tenth.

2. Water goes over Niagara Falls at a rate of 180 million cubic feet every $\frac{1}{2}$ hour. How much water goes over the Falls in 1 minute?

3. The value of the U.S. dollar in comparison to the value of foreign currency changes daily. Complete the table shown. Round to the nearest hundredth.

Euro	U.S. Dollar
1	1.07
	1.00
	6.00
6	
10	

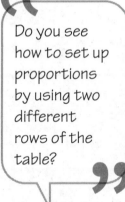

Do you see how to set up proportions by using two different rows of the table?

4. To make 4.5 cups of fruity granola, the recipe calls for 1.5 cups of raisins, 1 cup of granola, and 2 cups of blueberries. If you want to make 18 cups of fruity granola, how much of each of the ingredients do you need?

TALK the TALK

Choose Your Own Proportion Adventure

Write a problem situation for each proportion. Show the solution.

1. $\dfrac{8}{3} = \dfrac{2}{n}$

2. $\dfrac{\frac{1}{2}}{\frac{1}{4}} = \dfrac{h}{1}$

Assignment

Write

Describe a situation in which you would use each.

1. variable
2. means and extremes
3. inverse operations
4. isolate the variable

Remember

To solve a proportion means to determine all the values of the variables that make the proportion true.

You can rewrite a proportion as the product of the means and extremes.

If $\frac{a}{b} = \frac{c}{d}$, then $bc = ad$.

Practice

Write and solve a proportion to answer each question.

1. Carmen is making a strawberry drink. The recipe calls for 5 parts strawberry juice to 3 parts water. Carmen would like to make 64 fluid ounces of the strawberry drink. How many fluid ounces of strawberry juice and water does Carmen need?
2. Elena is making a grape drink. The recipe calls for 2 parts grape juice concentrate to 6 parts water. Elena would like to make 80 fluid ounces of the grape drink. How many fluid ounces of grape juice concentrate and water does Elena need?
3. Jose is making a trail mix. The recipe calls for 3 parts golden raisins to 2 parts cashews. Jose would like to make 30 cups of trail mix. How many cups of golden raisins and cashews does Jose need?
4. Miguel is making a snack mix. The recipe calls for 6 parts of spicy tortilla chips to 3 parts of corn chips. Miguel would like to make 45 cups of snack mix. How many cups of spicy tortilla chips and corn chips does Miguel need?
5. Carla is making a bean salad. The recipe calls for 4 parts green beans to 3 parts yellow wax beans. Carla would like to make 56 ounces of bean salad. How many ounces of green beans and yellow wax beans does Carla need?
6. Shawna is making smoothies. The recipe calls for 2 parts yogurt to 3 parts blueberries. Shawna wants to make 10 cups of smoothie mix. How many cups of yogurt and blueberries does Shawna need?

Stretch

The word *four* has 4 letters, so the number-to-letter-count ratio for 4 is 1 : 1, or just 1. Are there any other numbers between 1 and 20 that have equal number-to-letter-count ratios? What are they?

Review

1. The table shows the gallons filled in a pool over time.

   a. Complete the table.

Number of Hours	$\frac{1}{8}$	$\frac{1}{4}$	$\frac{1}{2}$	$\frac{5}{8}$
Gallons Filled			500	

   b. Determine a unit rate for this situation.

2. Pi is the ratio of what two measures of a circle?

3. Which is a better deal—a 16-inch diameter pizza for $12.99 or an 8-inch diameter pizza for $6?

4. Evaluate each expression for $g = 10$.

   a. $9 - 4g + 1$

   b. $\frac{20}{g} \div g + (8 - 5)$

Fractional Rates Summary

KEY TERMS

- complex ratio
- proportion
- variable

- means
- extremes
- solve a proportion

- isolate the variable
- inverse operations

LESSON 1	Making Punch

A rate is a ratio that compares quantities with different units. A unit rate is a rate in which the numerator or denominator (or both) is 1. Two or more ratios or rates can be compared.

For example, two friends make lemon-lime punch using the following recipes.

Jade's Recipe	Kim's Recipe
1 cup lemon-lime concentrate 3 cups club soda	2 cups lemon-lime concentrate 5 cups club soda

Determine which recipe has the stronger taste of lemon-lime.

For Jade's recipe, the ratio of lemon-lime to club soda is 1 cup : 3 cups, so the unit rate is $\frac{1}{3}$ cup lemon-lime per 1 cup club soda. For Kim's recipe, the ratio of lemon-lime to club soda is 2 cups : 5 cups, so the unit rate is $\frac{2}{5}$ cup lemon-lime per 1 cup club soda.

$\frac{1}{3} < \frac{2}{5}$, so Kim's recipe has the stronger taste of lemon-lime.

A unit rate can be represented by the ordered pair (1, r) on a coordinate plane.

For example, the graph shows the ratios of lemon-lime to club soda for Jade's and Kim's recipes.

The point (1, $\frac{1}{3}$) represents the unit rate for Jade's recipe, and the point (1, $\frac{2}{5}$) represents the unit rate for Kim's recipe.

The graph of Kim's line is steeper than the graph of Jade's line, which shows that Kim's recipe has a stronger taste of lemon-lime.

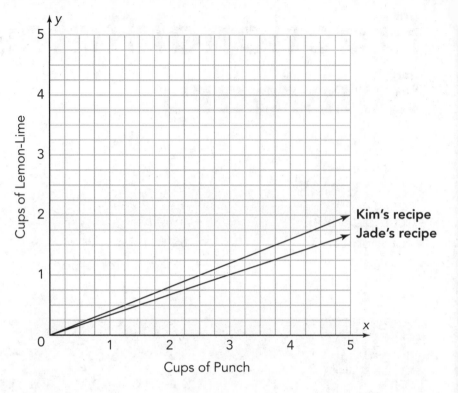

LESSON

2

Eggzactly!

A ratio in which one or both of the quantities being compared are written as fractions is called a **complex ratio**.

For example, traveling $\frac{1}{2}$ mile in $\frac{1}{4}$ hour represents a ratio of fractions, or a complex ratio. You can write this ratio, which is also a rate, in fractional form: $\frac{\frac{1}{2}}{\frac{1}{4}}$.

To convert a complex rate to a unit rate, you can multiply the numerator and denominator by the reciprocal of the denominator, or you can use the definition of division.

For example, the unit rate for traveling $\frac{1}{2}$ mile in $\frac{1}{4}$ hour is 2 miles per hour.

$$\frac{\frac{1}{2}}{\frac{1}{4}} \times \frac{\frac{4}{1}}{\frac{4}{1}} = \frac{\frac{4}{2}}{1}$$

$$= 2$$

$$\frac{\frac{1}{2}}{\frac{1}{4}} = \frac{1}{2} \div \frac{1}{4}$$

$$= \frac{1}{2} \cdot 4 = 2$$

To compare unit rates that are given in different units, you can use proportions and conversion rates.

For example, an ostrich can run 22 miles in $\frac{1}{2}$ hour. The Greater Roadrunner can run 300 yards in $\frac{1}{2}$ minute. Which bird runs faster?

The rate of the ostrich is already measured in miles and hours. You can set up a proportion and scale the original rate up to 1 hour.

The ostrich's speed is 44 miles per hour.

The rate of the Greater Roadrunner is written in yards per minute. You can use conversion rates to rewrite the rate in miles per hour.

The Greater Roadrunner's speed is about 20.5 miles per hour.

The ostrich runs faster.

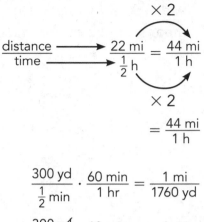

$$\frac{300 \text{ yd}}{\frac{1}{2} \text{ min}} \cdot \frac{60 \text{ min}}{1 \text{ hr}} = \frac{1 \text{ mi}}{1760 \text{ yd}}$$

$$\frac{300 \text{ yd}}{\frac{1}{2} \text{ min}} \cdot \frac{60 \text{ min}}{1 \text{ hr}} = \frac{1 \text{ mi}}{1760 \text{ yd}}$$

$$\frac{300}{\frac{1}{2}} \cdot \frac{60}{1} = \frac{1 \text{ mi}}{1760 \text{ hr}}$$

$$600 \cdot \frac{60}{1} \cdot \frac{1 \text{ mi}}{1760 \text{ hr}} \approx \frac{20.5 \text{ mi}}{1 \text{ hr}}$$

<table>
<tr><td>LESSON
3</td><td>Tagging Sharks</td></tr>
</table>

A **proportion** is an equation that states that two ratios are equal. A **variable** is a letter or symbol used to represent a number. A proportion of the form $\frac{a}{b} = \frac{c}{d}$ can be written in many different ways. Another example is $\frac{d}{b} = \frac{c}{a}$ or $\frac{c}{a} = \frac{d}{b}$.

In a proportion that is written $a : b = c : d$, the product of the two values in the middle (the **means**) equals the product of the two values on the outside (the **extremes**).

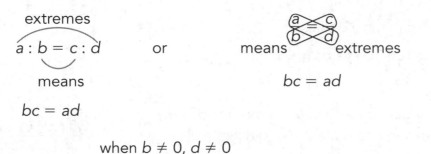

when $b \neq 0, d \neq 0$

To **solve a proportion** means to determine all the values of the variables that make the proportion true.

For example, you can rewrite the proportion $\frac{7 \text{ books}}{14 \text{ days}} = \frac{3 \text{ books}}{6 \text{ days}}$ as the product of the means equal to the product of the extremes.

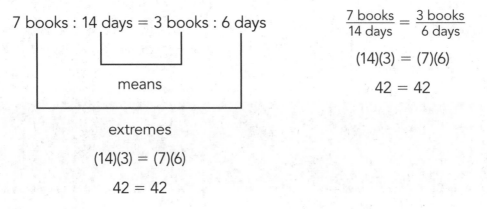

When you **isolate the variable** in an equation, you perform an operation, or operations, to get the variable by itself on one side of the equals sign. Multiplication and division are inverse operations. **Inverse operations** are operations that "undo" each other.

In the proportion $\frac{a}{b} = \frac{c}{d}$, you can multiply both sides by b to isolate the variable a.

$$b \cdot \frac{a}{b} = \frac{c}{d} \cdot b \longrightarrow a = \frac{cb}{d}$$

Another strategy is to multiply the means and extremes, and then isolate the variable by performing inverse operations.

$$\frac{a}{b} = \frac{c}{d}$$
$$ad = bc$$
$$\frac{ad}{d} = \frac{bc}{d}$$
$$a = \frac{bc}{d}$$

TOPIC 3

Proportionality

Equivalent ratios and direct variation are vital to chemists. Too much of one solution can result in a smoldering reaction, while too little of a solution may not result in a reaction at all.

Lesson 1

How Does Your Garden Grow?

Proportional Relationships. M1-91

Lesson 2

Complying with Title IX

Constant of Proportionality M1-109

Lesson 3

Fish-Inches

Identifying the Constant of Proportionality in Graphs. M1-127

Lesson 4

Minding Your Ps and Qs

Constant of Proportionality in Multiple Representations M1-139

Module 1: Thinking Proportionally

TOPIC 3: PROPORTIONALITY

In this topic, students learn about the constant of proportionality: the ratio between the two quantities being compared. They recognize that the constant is determined by the order of the ratio elements, and they use proportions to write and analyze direct variation equations. Students graph proportional relationships and determine the constant of proportionality from the graphs, interpreting this constant, the unit rate, in terms of the problem situation. Students practice determining if relationships are proportional, interpreting the meaning of linear proportional relationships, and determining and interpreting the constant of proportionality.

Where have we been?

In grade 6, students developed a strong understanding of ratio and rate reasoning, including reasoning about equivalent ratios from graphs and tables. In the previous topic, students reviewed some of these basic ideas and developed a formal strategy for solving proportions.

Where are we going?

Students will continue to apply the constant of proportionality to solve multistep ratio and percent problems in the next topic. They will solve percent problems using the constant of proportionality and direct variation and relate the constant of proportionality to the scale factor in scale drawings. The characteristics of proportional relationships, their graphs, and their equations provide the underpinnings of algebra and the study of functions.

Using a Diagram to Represent a Proportional Relationship

The diagram shows that there are 4 times as many dimes as nickels. Also, the total number of coins (40) is 8 times the number of nickels and twice the number of dimes.

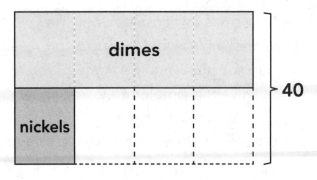

Myth: Asking questions means you don't understand.

It is universally true that, for any given body of knowledge, there are levels to understanding. For example, you might understand the rules of baseball and follow a game without trouble. But there is probably more to the game that you can learn. For example, do you know the 23 ways to get on first base, including the one where the batter strikes out?

Questions don't always indicate a lack of understanding. Instead, they might allow you to learn even more on a subject that you already understand. Asking questions may also give you an opportunity to ensure that you understand a topic correctly. Finally, questions are extremely important to ask yourself. For example, everyone should be in the habit of asking themselves, "Does that make sense? How would I explain it to a friend?"

#mathmythbusted

Talking Points

You can further support your student's learning by asking questions about the work they do in class or at home. Your student is learning to reason using proportions.

Questions to Ask

- How does this problem look like something you did in class?
- Can you show me the strategy you used to solve this problem? Do you know another way to solve it?
- Does your answer make sense? How do you know?
- Is there anything you don't understand? How can you use today's lesson to help?

Key Terms

direct variation
A situation represents a direct variation if the ratio between the y-value and its corresponding x-value is constant for every point.

constant of proportionality
In a proportional relationship, the ratio of all y-values to their corresponding x-values is constant. This ratio is called the constant of proportionality.

How Does Your Garden Grow?

Proportional Relationships

WARM UP

1. A bus travels 18 miles in 15 minutes. At the same rate, what distance will the bus travel in 50 minutes?

2. A copy machine averages 210 copies in 5 minutes. At the same rate, how many copies can the machine make in 12 minutes?

LEARNING GOALS

- Use tables and graphs to explore proportional relationships.
- Decide whether two quantities are in a proportional relationship by testing for equivalent ratios in a table.
- Decide whether two quantities are in a proportional relationship by graphing on a coordinate plane and observing whether the graph is a straight line through the origin.

KEY TERMS

- origin
- proportional relationship
- direct variation

You have learned about the relationship between ratios, a comparison of two quantities, and proportions. How can you determine if a proportional relationship exists between two quantities?

Keep on Mixing!

Amount of Bluish Green Paint	Amount of Yellow Paint	Amount of Blue Paint
3 pt	1 pt	2 pt
5 pt	2 pt	3 pt
6 pt	2 pt	4 pt
12 pt	4 pt	8 pt
15 pt	6 pt	9 pt
20 pt	8 pt	12 pt

The students in Mr. Raith's art class created various quantities of bluish green paint using pints of yellow and blue paint.

The table shows the different mixtures of paint, in pints, that the students made.

1. How many different shades of paint did the students make? How do you know?

2. Some of the shades of the paint are more yellow than others. Which mixture(s) are the most yellow? Explain your reasoning.

The **origin** is a point on a graph with the ordered pair (0, 0).

3. Plot an ordered pair for each bluish green paint mixture. Draw a line connecting each point to the origin. What do you notice?

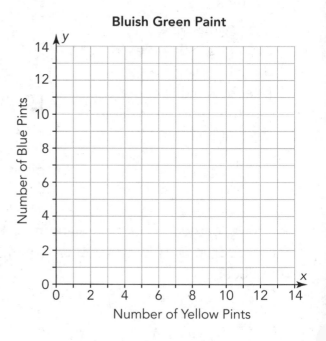

Bluish Green Paint

Representations of Varying Quantities

The student government association (SGA) at Radloff Middle School is creating an urban garden at their school for use by their community. They divided up into groups to design different parts of the garden and were asked to (1) describe their project, (2) create an equation to model part of their design or to answer a question about their design, and (3) sketch a graph of their equation.

1. Isaac, the president of the SGA, mixed up the representations of the projects after they were submitted to him. Help Isaac match the scenarios, equations, and graphs.

   • Cut out the scenarios, equations, and graphs at the end of the lesson.

   • Sort the scenarios, equations, and graphs into corresponding groups.

   • Tape the representations into the table provided.

When you connect an equation to a graph, you are establishing a dependency between the quantities. Remember, the independent quantity is always represented on the x-axis.

Scenario			
Equation			
Graph			
Table			

ACTIVITY 1.2

Defining Proportional Relationships

When looking over the submissions from the urban garden working groups, Isaac notices that there are two different types of graphical relationships represented: linear and non-linear.

1. **Classify each group's graph as representing a linear or a non-linear relationship between quantities.**

Isaac notices that the linear graphs are slightly different but he doesn't know why. He decides to analyze a table of values for each linear graph.

2. **Create a table of at least 4 values for each linear relationship in the urban garden project.**

Isaac knows that simple equations can represent additive or multiplicative relationships between quantities.

3. **Analyze the equations.**

   a. **Based on the equations, which graph represents an additive relationship between the variables and which represents a multiplicative relationship?**

   b. **Which variable represents the independent (input) and which represents the dependent (output).**

One special type of relationship that compares quantities using multiplicative reasoning is a ratio relationship. When two equivalent ratios are set equal to each other, they form a proportion. The quantities in the proportion are in a **proportional relationship**.

You can decide if two quantities are in a proportional relationship by testing that all ratios, $\frac{y}{x}$ or $\frac{x}{y}$, in a table of values are equivalent.

For a relationship to illustrate a proportional relationship, all the ratios $\frac{y}{x}$ or $\frac{x}{y}$, must represent the same constant.

4. Use your tables of values in Question 2 to determine which, if any, of the linear relationships illustrate a proportional relationship. Show the values of the ratios in each relationship.

Isaac says the equation $y = \pi r^2$ represents a proportional relationship between y and r because it includes multiplication between a numerical coefficient and a variable expression.

5. Use a table of values and corresponding ratios in the form of $\frac{y}{x}$ to explain why Isaac is incorrect.

6. Explain to Isaac how the graphs in the urban garden design project are different. Include the terms *linear relationship* and *non-linear relationship*, *proportional relationship*, and *equivalent ratios*.

In this activity you will analyze three different problem situations and then determine which represents a proportional relationship.

Bob and his little brother Jake want to build bird feeders to sell at a local farmers market. They have enough money to buy materials to build 10 bird feeders.

1. Complete a table of values by listing possible ways in which they can divide up the work. Assume that each brother only makes whole bird feeders. Then complete the graph.

Bird Feeders Built by Bob	Bird Feeders Built by Jake

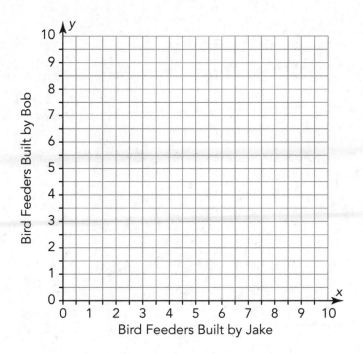

You can draw a line through your points to model the relationship. Then *decide* if all the points make sense in terms of the problem situation.

2. Describe how the number of bird feeders built by Bob affects the number Jake builds.

3. What is the ratio of bird feeders that Bob builds to the number that Jake builds? Explain your reasoning.

4. Dontrell claims that the number of bird feeders Bob builds is proportional to the number of bird feeders Jake builds. Do you agree with Dontrell's claim? Explain your reasoning.

Vanessa was given a math problem to determine how many different rectangles can be constructed with an area of 12 square inches.

5. Vanessa thinks that there are only two: one with a width of 2 inches and a length of 6 inches, and another with a width of 3 inches and a length of 4 inches.
   Is she correct? Explain your reasoning.

6. Complete a table of values for the width and length of a rectangle with an area of 12 square inches. Then complete the graph.

Width of Rectangle (in.)	Length of Rectangle (in.)

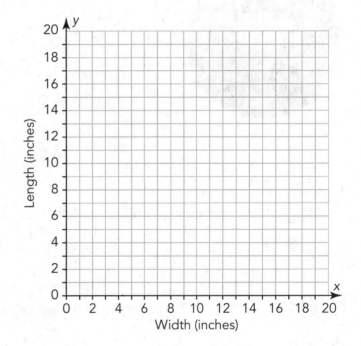

7. Describe how the width of the rectangle affects the length of the rectangle.

8. Do the width and length of a rectangle with an area of 12 square inches form a proportional relationship? Explain your reasoning.

One species of bamboo can grow at an average rate of 60 centimeters per day.

9. Complete a table of values using the given growth rate of the bamboo plant. Then complete the graph.

> Why do you think this problem says "average rate" instead of just rate?

Time (days)	Height of Bamboo (cm)

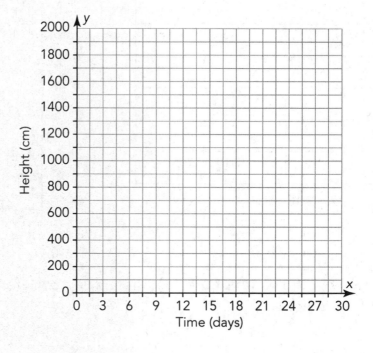

10. Describe how the time affects the height of the bamboo plant.

11. Is the number of days of growth proportional to the height of the bamboo plant? Explain your reasoning.

ACTIVITY 1.4 Direct Variation

You saw that the height of a bamboo plant varies based on the number of days the bamboo grows. For example, for each increase in one day, the bamboo grows 60 centimeters.

A situation represents a **direct variation** if the ratio between the y-value and its corresponding x-value is constant for every point. If two quantities vary directly, the points on a graph form a straight line, and the line passes through the origin.

You can describe the quantities of a direct variation relationship as directly proportional.

Examine the worked example.

WORKED EXAMPLE

A car driving at a constant rate of 60 miles per hour is an example of direct variation. The distance varies directly as time.

A sketch of a graph that could represent this situation is shown.

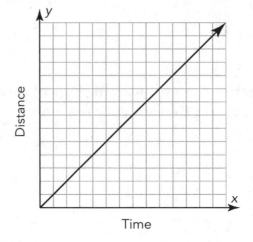

When you sketch a graph, be sure to include the labels for each axis. However, you don't *always* have to show values.

1. Explain how the situation in the worked example is an example of a direct variation.

> Think about how the quantities relate to each other at any given point.

2. Explain how you can use each graph in the previous activity, *Proportional or Not?*, to determine which scenarios represent direct variations.

3. List another example of quantities that vary directly. Then, sketch a graph that could represent the relationship between the quantities.

TALK the TALK 💬

Determining Proportionality from Tables and Graphs

Go back and examine the graphs in this lesson. Do you see a pattern?

1. How are all the graphs that display proportional relationships the same?

2. Sketch a graph that displays a proportional relationship.

3. Which tables display linear relationships? Which display proportional relationships? Explain your reasoning.

a.

x	y
1	10
2	11
4	13
5	14

b.

x	y
0	0
1	6
3	18
4	24

c.

x	y
0	4
1	8
2	12
3	16

d.

x	y
1	30
2	15
4	10
5	5

Cutouts for The Urban Garden Project

✂ -

Group A is designing one section of the garden to include fresh herbs grown in circular beds. The group needs to determine the area of each herb bed given the radius of the bed.

Group B is developing a plan to landscape the perimeter of the urban garden. They could only find a meter stick broken at 6 cm, so they reported the dimensions of the garden based on the measurements read off the meter stick. This group needs to determine the actual side lengths of the garden.

Group C is designing the vegetable patches and have decided that each rectangular vegetable patch will be 5 inches wide for every 8 inches long. This group needs to determine the possible dimensions for the lengths of the vegetable patches.

$$y = 1.6x$$

$$y = \pi x^2$$

$$y = x + 6$$

Assignment

Write

Explain how the following terms are related: linear relationship, proportional relationship, equivalent ratios, and direct variation.

Remember

For a graph to represent a proportional relationship, the points of the graph must form a straight line and pass through the origin of the graph.

For a table of values to represent a proportional relationship, all the ratios of corresponding x- and y-values must be constant.

Practice

1. Analyze each table shown. Determine if the relationship is proportional. If the relationship is proportional, state the constant ratio for the relationship.

   a. Of the 75 boys in the 7th grade class, 25 participate in at least one sport. Of the 120 girls in the 7th grade class, 30 participate in at least one sport.

   b. Of the 210 boys in the 8th grade, 190 have a cell phone. Of the 168 girls in the 8th grade, 152 have a cell phone.

7th Grade Class	Plays Sports	Total
Boys	25	75
Girls	30	120

8th Grade Class	Cell Phones	Total
Boys	190	210
Girls	152	168

2. Match each graph with its scenario. Then state if the scenario represents a linear relationship. If it represents a linear relationship, state if it represents a proportional relationship.

   a. Vanessa and Michelle must decide how to divide 16 marbles among themselves.

   b. The perimeter of a square is 4 times the length of one side of the square.

   c. The area of a square is calculated by squaring the length of one side of the square.

   d. When Tara, a nurse, works on Saturdays, she is paid a $30 bonus plus $40 per hour worked.

Graph A   Graph B   Graph C   Graph D

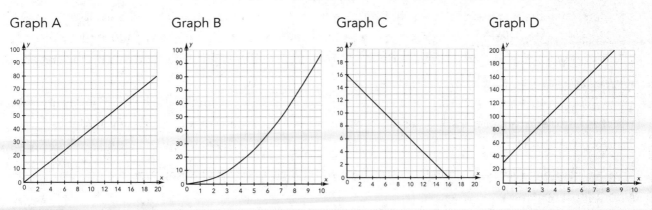

3. In 2010, Chevrolet produced 12,194 Corvettes. That means they made about 34 Corvettes per day.

    a. Create a table to show the number of Corvettes made in at least 5 different numbers of days.

    b. Use the table to determine if this situation represents a proportional relationship.

    c. Use the data in the table to create a graph of the total number of Corvettes produced over time.

    d. Does the number of Corvettes vary directly with the number of days? Explain using the graph.

Stretch

Another way to classify varying quantities is as an inverse variation, or inversely proportional. The tables shown represent inverse variations. Study the tables of values and make a conjecture about the relationship between the quantities that illustrate inverse variation.

Number of Hours	Number of People
2	6
3	4
$\frac{1}{12}$	144

Width of Rectangle	Length of Rectangle
2	18
12	3
0.5	72

Review

Use proportions to solve each.

1. In the town of Clover, 3 out of 5 citizens who are eligible to vote did so in the fall election.

    a. Determine the number of citizens that voted in the fall election if 400 citizens were eligible.

    b. Determine the number of citizens that were eligible to vote in the fall election if 180 actually voted.

2. The student council at Camp Creek Middle School determines that 3 out of 4 students prefer that all school assemblies be held on Friday afternoon.

    a. If 200 students are surveyed, how many will prefer that school assemblies be held on Friday afternoon?

    b. If 747 students prefer the school assemblies be held on Friday afternoon, how many students were surveyed?

Write a unit rate to represent the relationship between the given quantities. Round to the nearest hundredth, if necessary.

3. 2.5 liters ≈ 0.66 gallon

4. 430.6 centimeters ≈ 169.5 inches

Determine each quotient.

5. 67.36 ÷ 3.2

6. 3401.74 ÷ 7.9

Complying with Title IX

Constant of Proportionality

Warm Up

Washington Middle School collects canned food for a local community food bank. Last year, there were 180 students enrolled at the school and they collected 102 cans of food.

1. Write the ratio representing the number of cans of food contributed to the total number of students in the school.

2. What is the unit rate of cans contributed per student?

3. This year, 210 students are enrolled in the school. Assume the number of cans of food contributed per student for both years is the same. How many cans of food should the school expect to be contributed this year?

LEARNING GOALS

- Determine if there is a constant ratio between two variables.
- Identify the constant of proportionality in proportional relationships.
- Identify the constant of proportionality in equations.
- Represent proportional relationships by equations.

KEY TERM

- constant of proportionality

You know how to recognize proportional relationships from tables and graphs. How do you represent proportional relationships with equations?

Is It Proportional?

Analyze each table to determine if the relationship is proportional. If the table represents a proportional relationship, state the constant ratio that exists between corresponding values of the two quantities.

1. A 30-minute television show has 8 minutes of commercials and 22 minutes of the show. A 120-minute television movie has 32 minutes of commercials and 88 minutes of the movie.

Does the order in which you write your ratios, $\frac{x}{y}$ or $\frac{y}{x}$, matter when determining if a proportional relationship exists?

Total Program Length (minutes)	Actual Show Length (minutes)	Commercial Length (minutes)
30	22	8
120	88	32

2. There are 250 boys in 6th grade, and 75 are in the band. There are 200 girls in 6th grade, and 60 are in the band.

6th Grade Class	Total	Band
Boys	250	75
Girls	200	60

3. Commuters in McKnight and Mitenridge either drive to work or take public transportation.

Commuters	Drive to Work	Public Transportation to Work
McKnight	175	120
Mitenridge	525	300

4. Of the 250 middle-school boys who have a subscription to *Boys Noise*, 125 access the magazine through the website. Of the 280 middle-school girls who have a subscription to *Girls Rockstar*, 160 access the magazine through the website.

In a proportional relationship, the ratio of all *y*-values, or outputs, to their corresponding *x*-values, or inputs, is constant. This specific ratio, $\frac{y}{x}$, is called the **constant of proportionality**. Generally, the variable *k* is used to represent the constant of proportionality.

Let's revisit the television show scenario. This situation represents a proportional relationship.

> The input value is known, the output value is what you are trying to determine.

Total Program Length (minutes)	Actual Show Length (minutes)	Commercial Length (minutes)
30	22	8
120	88	32

Suppose you want to determine the actual lengths of your favorite television shows, without commercials, if you know the total program length.

1. **Identify the input and output quantities in this scenario.**

To determine the length of a program, without commercials, you will need to multiply the total program length by a constant of proportionality.

Analyze the different ideas for determining the constant of proportionality.

Jeremiah 👍

We want to know the actual show length and we know the total program length, so

$$k = \frac{22 \text{ minutes of show}}{30 \text{ minutes of total length}},$$

or $k = \frac{11}{15}$.

Keisha 👎

To determine if a proportional relationship exists the order of the ratio doesn't matter, so the constant of proportionality can be

$$k = \frac{15}{11}$$

or $k = \frac{11}{15}$.

Susan 👎

I think the constant of proportionality is

$$k = \frac{22 \text{ minutes of show}}{8 \text{ minutes of commercials}},$$

or $k = \frac{11}{4}$.

JAMie 👎

JEREMIAH'S CORRECT ABOUT WHICH NUMBERS TO USE BUT HE HAS THEM MIXED UP. THE CONSTANT OF PROPORTIONALITY IS

$$k = \frac{30 \text{ MINUTES OF TOTAL LENGTH}}{22 \text{ MINUTES OF SHOW}}, \text{ OR } k = \frac{15}{11}.$$

2. Explain why Susan's solution is incorrect.

3. Explain why Jeremiah is correct but Jamie and Keisha are incorrect.

> The term *proportional* is used often in the Title IX document. What does this mean for sports at schools?

In 1972, the federal government passed Title IX, a law requiring educational institutions that receive federal funds to provide equitable athletic opportunities for boys and girls. One of the requirements for compliance with Title IX is for institutions to provide opportunities for each gender that are *proportional* to their rates of enrollment or show that they are working to increase such opportunities. Similarly, male and female athletes are to receive athletic scholarship dollars *proportional* to their participation.

Let's think about the implications of Title IX at Vista Middle School.

There are 5 girls for every 6 boys enrolled in Vista Middle School.

1. Set up proportions for each question. Then, solve each proportion to determine the unknown value. Use the information from the ratio given.

   a. If there are 300 boys enrolled in the school, how many girls are enrolled in the school?

   b. If there are 325 girls enrolled in the school, how many boys are enrolled in the school?

2. Define variables for the quantities that are changing in this situation.

3. Set up a proportion using your variables for the quantities to the ratio given for the enrollment of girls to boys enrolled in Vista Middle School.

4. Use your proportion.

   a. Write an equation to determine the number of girls enrolled at Vista Middle School if you know the number of boys enrolled.

   b. What is the constant of proportionality in this situation? Where is the constant of proportionality in the equation?

   c. What does the constant of proportionality mean in this problem situation?

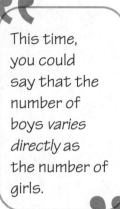

This time, you could say that the number of boys *varies directly* as the number of girls.

5. Use your proportion.

   a. Write an equation to determine the number of boys enrolled at Vista Middle School if you know the number of girls enrolled.

   b. What is the constant of proportionality in this situation? Where do you see the constant of proportionality in the equation?

   c. What does the constant of proportionality mean in this problem situation?

6. What do you notice about the constant of proportionality in each situation?

7. Do you think each constant of proportionality makes sense in terms of the problem situation?

Sometimes, the constant of proportionality is not a whole number. The constant of proportionality can also be a decimal or a fraction. When the constant of proportionality involves whole items, like people, it may seem strange to think about the constant of proportionality in terms of a fraction. Instead, you can think of the constant of proportionality as a way to predict outcomes of a situation.

8. Use your equations and the information about Title IX to answer each question.

   a. If there are opportunities for 79 boys to participate in athletics, how many opportunities must be available for girls?

   b. If there are opportunities for 119 girls to participate in athletics, how many opportunities must be available for boys?

> Did you use the constant of proportionality for the girls or for the boys? Does it matter which constant of proportionality you use?

Title IX addresses the number of athletics opportunities provided to each gender, but the actual participation at schools may differ. Also, the same person may participate in multiple sports.

At Vista Middle School, 5 out of every 7 girls play sports. The guidance counselor, Ms. Shanahan, and the athletics director, Coach Culpepper, are completing reports about the students at Vista Middle School.

Consider the information each person knows and use the constant of proportionality to write equations for each situation.

Guidance Counselor

Ms. Shanahan knows the number of girls in the school on a given day, and she needs to be able to calculate the expected number of girls who play sports.

Athletics Director

Coach Culpepper knows the number of girls participating in sports during a given season, and she needs to be able to calculate the expected number of total girls in the school.

1. Determine the constant of proportionality for each situation.

   a. Guidance Counselor

   b. Athletics Director

2. Define variables for the quantities that are changing in these situations.

3. Use the constants of proportionality to write equations to determine the information needed by each person.

   a. Guidance Counselor   b. Athletics Director

In terms of proportionality, Ms. Shanahan could state that the number of girls who play sports is proportional to the number of total girls in the school at a constant rate equal to the constant of proportionality.

4. Write Coach Culpepper's situation using the language of proportionality and include the value for the constant of proportionality.

5. Consider the given equations, where y represents the dependent or output quantity and x represents the independent or input quantity.

$$\frac{y}{x} = k$$

$$\frac{y}{x} = \frac{k}{1}$$

$$y = kx$$

   a. Describe how the first equation represents the constant of proportionality.

   b. Explain how the second equation represents proportional relationships.

   c. Describe how the first equation was rewritten to create the third equation.

   d. Explain the meaning of the constant of proportionality, k, in the third equation.

6. Identify the constant of proportionality in each equation and describe its meaning.

a. $d = 2r$, where d represents the diameter of a circle and r represents the radius of a circle.

b. $P = 3s$, where P represents the perimeter and s represents the sides of an equilateral triangle.

ACTIVITY
2.4

Using the Constant of Proportionality to Solve Problems

A chemist must use a solution that is 30% of reagent and 70% of water for an experiment. A solution is a mixture of two or more liquids. A reagent is a substance used in a chemical reaction to produce other substances.

1. Define variables for the quantities that are changing in this problem situation.

2. Write an equation for the amount of water needed based on the amount of reagent. What is the constant of proportionality?

3. Use your equation from Question 2 to write an equation for the amount of reagent needed based on the amount of water. Explain your reasoning.

In Question 3, you can say that the amount of reagent varies directly as the amount of water in the solution.

4. Use your equations to answer each question.

   a. If the chemist uses 6 liters of reagent, how many liters of water will she need to make her 30% solution?

   b. If the chemist uses 77 milliliters of water, how many milliliters of reagent will she need to make her 30% solution?

5. Write an equation to show that y is directly proportional to x using the constant of proportionality given. Then solve for the unknown value.

   a. $k = 0.7$ and $y = 4$

   b. $k = \frac{3}{11}$ and $x = 9$

   c. $k = 5$ and $x = 1\frac{1}{2}$

   d. $k = \frac{1}{6}$ and $y = 3\frac{1}{3}$

TALK the TALK

Turning the Tables

Consider the equation $y = kx$. Use the value of the constant of proportionality assigned to you to answer the questions. You will present your work to your class.

1. Write a scenario for a proportional relationship that would be represented by the equation. Clearly define your variables and identify the direction of the proportional relationship.

2. Interpret the constant of proportionality in the context of your scenario.

3. Write and solve at least 2 questions that could be solved using your equation.

Assignment

Write

Define *constant of proportionality* in your own words. Provide a specific example with your definition.

Remember

If y is directly proportional to x, the relationship can be represented by the equation $y = kx$, where k is the constant of proportionality.

Practice

1. Analyze each table or problem situation to determine if the relationship is proportional. State a constant of proportionality if possible. Show your work.

a.

Girls	Boys
7	14
9	21
11	22

b. A baby blue whale weighed 5520 pounds at birth. After two days, the baby weighed 5710. After 14 days, the baby weighed 8180 pounds.

2. Maya's construction company builds brick houses. The number of bricks her crew installs varies directly with the number of hours they work.

Hours Worked	Bricks Installed
8	1680
7	1470
6	1260

a. Define variables for the quantities that are changing in this problem situation.

b. Analyze the table to determine the constant of proportionality.

c. What does the constant of proportionality mean in this situation?

d. Write an equation to show the relationship between the number of hours worked, the number of bricks installed, and the constant of proportionality.

e. Use your equation to determine how many bricks Maya's crew can install in 5.5 hours.

f. Use your equation to determine how many hours it will take Maya's crew to install 840 bricks.

3. Given a value for the input variable, x, and the output variable, y, calculate the constant of proportionality.

a. $x = 21$ and $y = 6$

b. $x = 60$ and $y = 18$

c. $x = 2\frac{2}{5}$ and $y = 7\frac{1}{2}$

d. $x = 4\frac{8}{11}$ and $y = 3\frac{6}{11}$

4. The following is the recipe to make 6 cups of Perfect Lemonade:

- 1 cup sugar
- 1 cup water (for the simple syrup)
- 1 cup lemon juice
- 4 cups cold water (to dilute)

You want to analyze the relationship between the number of cups of sugar and the number of cups of lemonade.

a. Define variables for the quantities that are changing in this problem situation.

b. Set up a proportion using the ratio of cups of sugar to cups of lemonade.

c. Use your proportion to write an equation for the number of cups of sugar based on the number of cups of lemonade.

d. What is the constant of proportionality in this equation? What does it mean in this context?

e. Use your equation in (c) to write an equation for the number of cups of lemonade based on the number of cups of sugar.

f. What is the constant of proportionality in this equation? What does it mean in this context?

5. Dudley and Bob monitored the distance their pet turtle could walk in a certain amount of time. Their results are shown in the table. The table of values represents a proportional relationship.

Time (minutes)	Distance (inches)
5	14.5
14	40.6
19	55.1
25	72.5

a. Define variables for the quantities that are changing in this problem situation.

b. Write an equation for the distance traveled by the turtle based on the number of minutes.

c. What is the constant of proportionality in this equation? What does it mean in this context?

d. Use your equation in (b) to write an equation for the time it would take for the turtle to travel a given distance.

e. What is the constant of proportionality in this equation? What does it mean in this context?

Stretch

If a varies inversely as b, then the product of a and b is constant. Use direct and inverse variation to solve this problem.

If x varies inversely as y and varies directly with z, and if y and z are both 3 when $x = 5$, what is the value of $z - y$ when $x = 8$?

Review

1. Sketch a graph that represents a linear, non-proportional relationship. Label your quantities.

2. Sketch a graph that represents a direct variation relationship. Label your quantities.

3. Jonah will be staying a month in one of the cities listed in the table. He wants to determine the average cost of public transportation for each city. He finds the following information.

City	Cost for Unlimited Public Transportation
New York City	$51.50 for 14 days
Miami	$100 for 1 month
Los Angeles	$17 for 1 week
Chicago	$14 for 3 days

   a. Calculate the unit rate, or per day cost, for unlimited transportation in each city. (Let 1 week = 7 days and 1 month = 30 days.)

   b. If Jonah stays in the city for a month, how much would he spend on transportation in each city?

4. Plot each ordered pair on a coordinate plane.

   a. A (1, 4.75)

   b. $B\left(\frac{7}{2}, 1\right)$

   c. C (−2, 8)

   d. $D\left(-4, -\frac{1}{2}\right)$

   e. E (0, 0)

   f. $F\left(5, -\frac{5}{2}\right)$

Fish-Inches

Identifying the Constant of Proportionality in Graphs

WARM UP

Solve each equation for the variable.

1. $\frac{1}{2}a = 5$

2. $\frac{p}{\frac{1}{3}} = 2$

3. $3x = \frac{3}{2}$

4. $\frac{6}{z} = \frac{1}{6}$

LEARNING GOALS

- Determine if relationships represented in words, tables, equations, or graphs are proportional.
- Interpret the meaning of linear proportional relationships represented in words, tables, equations, and graphs.
- Identify and interpret the constant of proportionality for quantities that are proportional and represented in words, tables, equations, and graphs.
- Explain what a point on the graph of a proportional relationship means in terms of the problem situation.
- Explain what the points (0, 0) and (1, r) mean on the graph of a proportional relationship, where r is the unit rate.

You have determined the constant of proportionality in problem situations and from equations. How can you represent the constant of proportionality in graphs?

The Fish-Inches System of Measurement

You are thinking of purchasing an aquarium. You contact the owner of an aquarium store. You need to know how many fish to purchase for an aquarium, but first you must determine how big the aquarium will be. The owner of the aquarium store tells you his rule of thumb is to purchase "a total length of fish of 3 inches for each 2 gallons of water in the aquarium."

1. **How many gallons of water would you need if you had a 4-inch fish and a 2-inch fish? Draw a diagram to explain your reasoning.**

Drawing a model would be really helpful here.

2. **Define variables for the quantities that are changing in this problem situation.**

3. **Write an equation for each:**

   a. **fish-inches based on the gallons of water**

   b. **gallons of water based on fish-inches**

4. Use one of your equations to solve each problem.

   a. If an aquarium holds 10 gallons of water, how many fish-inches should you purchase?

   b. If you want to purchase a 5-inch fish, two 2-inch fish, and three 3-inch fish, how many gallons of water should the aquarium hold?

5. Determine the constant of proportionality given by each equation and explain what it means in context.

ACTIVITY 3.1 Graphs of Two Constants of Proportionality

Let's graph each equation you wrote in the previous activity.

1. Create a table of ordered pairs. Then plot the ordered pairs to create a graph of each equation.

Fish-Inches							
Gallons							

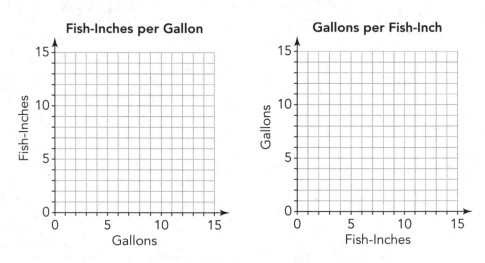

2. What does the point (0, 0) mean on each graph?

3. Determine the meaning of each point.

   a. What does the point (6, 9) on the Fish-Inches per Gallon graph represent?

   b. What does the point (9, 6) on the Gallons per Fish-Inch graph represent?

c. What does the point $(1, 1\frac{1}{2})$ on the Fish-Inches per Gallon graph represent?

d. What does the point $(1, \frac{2}{3})$ on the Gallons per Fish-Inch graph represent?

4. What is the unit rate for each graph? Explain how you can determine the unit rate using the graph.

5. Use one of your graphs to determine each answer.

   a. How many inches of fish can fit into 10 gallons of water?

   b. How many gallons are needed for $7\frac{1}{2}$ inches of fish?

The constant of proportionality is represented on the graph, too. Can you locate it?

6. Use one of the graphs to estimate each answer. Explain how you used the graph to determine your estimate.

   a. How many gallons would be needed for 16 inches of fish?

   b. How many inches of fish would fit into 16 gallons?

ACTIVITY
3.2

Constant of Proportionality from a Graph

The graph shown displays the relationship between the time and distance Ella runs.

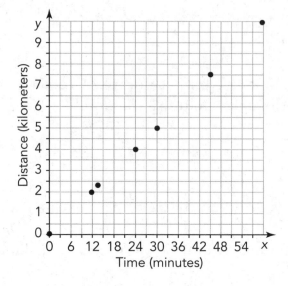

1. Define variables and write an equation to represent the relationship between Ella's distance and time.

2. Use your equation to answer each question.

   a. How far can Ella run in 15 minutes?

b. How long does it take Ella to run 7.5 kilometers?

c. How far can Ella run in one hour?

d. Determine the constant of proportionality in kilometers per hour. Then, write another equation representing Ella's distance (*d*) varies directly with time (*t*).

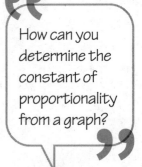

How can you determine the constant of proportionality from a graph?

e. How is this equation the same as, and different from, the previous equation you wrote?

Determining Proportional Relationships from Graphs

A graph establishes dependency. So, if the graph shows a proportional relationship, then y varies directly as x.

You have seen that proportional relationships can be represented on graphs and that the constant of proportionality can be identified from the graph.

1. Determine if each graph shows a proportional relationship between x and y. If possible, determine the constant of proportionality. Explain how you determined your answer.

a.

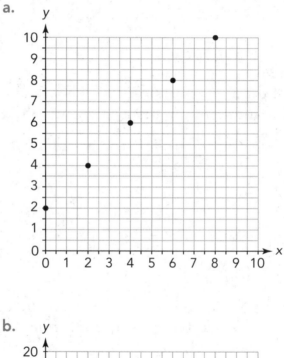

b.

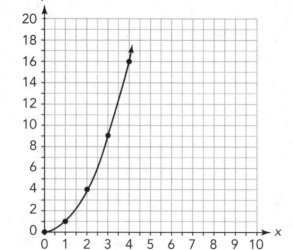

c.

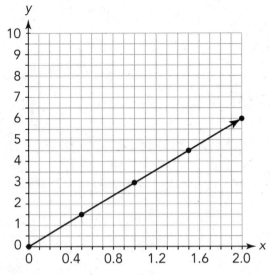

d.

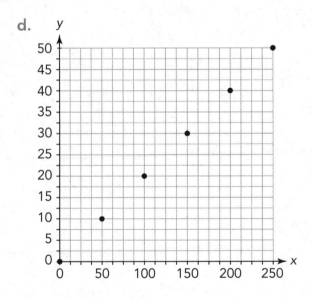

TALK the TALK

How Do You Know?

Use examples to explain your answer to each question.

1. Given a graph of a relationship between two quantities, how do you know:

    a. if the graph shows a proportional relationship?

    b. what the constant of proportionality is?

    c. what the unit rate is?

    d. what any ordered pair on the graph represents?

Assignment

Write

Given a graph of a proportional relationship, the quotient of the *y*-value of any ordered pair divided by the *x*-value of that ordered pair is the constant of proportionality. Explain why.

Remember

When the relationship between two quantities is proportional, the graph of the relationship is a straight line that passes through the origin. The point $(1, r)$ represents the unit rate and the ratio $\frac{r}{1}$ represents the constant of proportionality, k.

Practice

Determine the constant of proportionality k and interpret it in the context of each problem.

1. The graph shows the relationship between the distance in miles between you and a storm and the number of seconds between when you see lightning and when you hear thunder.

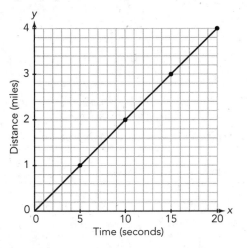

2. The graph shows the relationship between the number of euros Jason received and the number of dollars Jason exchanged during his trip to Spain.

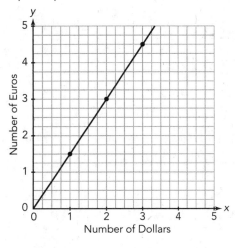

3. The graph shows the relationship between the weight of an object on Earth and the weight of the same object object on Venus.

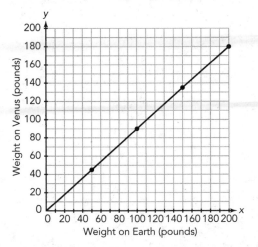

4. The graph shows the relationship between the area of a room in square feet and the cost of covering the floor with new tile.

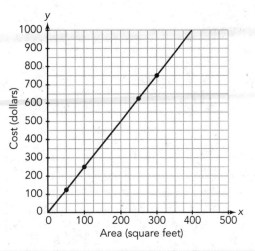

5. The graph shows the relationship between the cups of water and pounds of beef needed for a beef casserole.

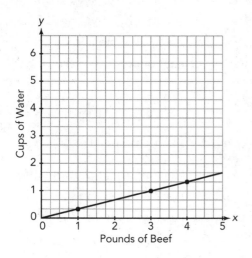

6. The graph shows the relationship between the number of posters in a classroom and the number of thumbtacks used to hold them up.

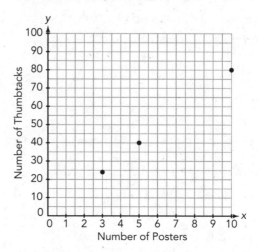

Stretch

At any given time of the day, the length of your shadow is proportional to your height. Suppose a person who is 81 inches tall casts a shadow that is 94.5 inches long. Another person in the same place casts a shadow that is 84 inches long. How tall is the second person?

Review

1. Use the equation for the constant of proportionality, $k = \frac{y}{x}$, to determine each unknown value.

   a. $k = \frac{3}{2}$ and $y = 15$

   b. $k = \frac{1}{4}$ and $y = 5$

2. Determine a unit rate for each scenario.

   a. $\frac{3}{4}$ of an inch of rain fell in $\frac{1}{2}$ hour.

   b. Heather charges a half-dollar for each eighth of a pizza.

3. Simplify each expression.

   a. $8 - 4(5) + 2^4$

   b. $10 \div (1 + 4) - 3^2$

Minding Your Ps and Qs

4

Constant of Proportionality in Multiple Representations

WARM UP

Solve each equation.

1. $5p = 2.5$

2. $\frac{1}{3}j = 9$

3. $0.12k = 10.08$

4. $8k = 0$

LEARNING GOALS

- Determine if relationships represented in words, tables, equations, or graphs are proportional.
- Interpret the meaning of linear proportional relationships represented in words, tables, equations, and graphs.
- Determine and interpret the constant of proportionality for quantities that are proportional and represented in words, tables, equations, and graphs.

You have learned how to determine the constant of proportionality. How can you solve problems using this constant in tables, graphs, and diagrams?

Penny's Nickels Are a Quarter of Her Dimes

Penny collects only nickels and dimes. She has one-quarter as many nickels as dimes.

A diagram can represent this problem situation.

All together she has 40 coins. How much money does she have?

1. Explain how you can use the diagram to solve the problem. Determine the solution.

2. Write an equation to represent the proportional relationship between:

   a. the number of nickels and the number of dimes.

   b. the number of dimes and the total number of coins.

   c. the number of nickels and the total number of coins.

3. Identify the constant of proportionality in each proportional relationship described in Question 2.

ACTIVITY
4.1

Using a Graph to Write an Equation

NOTES

The graph shows Natasha's total number of free throw attempts and the total number of free throws made.

Natasha's Free Throws

1. Explain how you know the graph represents a relationship that is proportional.

2. Determine the constant of proportionality and describe what it represents in this problem situation.

3. If Natasha attempted 30 free throws, how many would she probably make? First, use your graph to estimate the answer. Then, verify your answer by using an equation.

ACTIVITY
4.2

Using an Equation to Create a Table

Another example of a proportional relationship is the relationship between the number of hours a worker works and his or her wages earned in dollars.

The amount of money (m) Shaylah earns varies directly with the number of hours (h) she works. The equation describing this relationship is $m = 9.25h$.

1. **What does the constant of proportionality represent in this situation?**

2. **Complete the table based on the equation given. Include the constant of proportionality in the table.**

Hours Worked	Earnings (dollars)
0	
	112.85
40	

During the summer, Fernando works as a movie attendant. The number of hours he works varies each week.

3. Write an equation to represent this situation. Then complete the table based on your equation and include the constant of proportionality.

Hours Worked	Earnings (dollars)
3	26.88

4. What is the constant of proportionality? What does it mean in this problem situation?

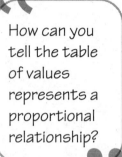

How can you tell the table of values represents a proportional relationship?

| ACTIVITY 4.3 | Using a Table to Create a Scenario |

Analyze the given table.

Number of Windows	Amount of Window Cleaner (ounces)
0	0
2	16
3	24
4	32
5	40
6	48

1. Describe one possible situation that could be represented by this table of values. Include how the quantities relate to each other.

2. What is the constant of proportionality and what does it represent in your situation?

3. If the table values were used to create a graph, how would the points appear?

Using a Scenario to Write an Equation

A baby elephant nurses for the first two years of its life. It drinks about 10 liters of milk every day.

1. Define variables and write an equation to represent the relationship between the amounts of milk the baby elephant consumes and the time it spends consuming the milk. Assume the elephant maintains the same rate of consumption.

2. Identify the constant of proportionality and describe what it means in this situation.

3. Create a graph to represent this situation.

The weight of person on Earth varies directly as the weight of an object on the Moon. A 150-pound person would weigh approximately 25 pounds on the Moon.

4. Define variables and write and equation to represent the relationship between the weight of an object on Earth and the weight of an object on the Moon.

5. Identify the constant of proportionality and describe what it means in this situation.

6. Create a graph to represent this situation.

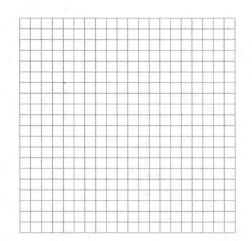

Multiple Representations of Proportional Relationships

Suppose *q* varies directly as *p*.

1. Complete the table for variables *p* and *q*.

p	q
0	
2	6
4	12
0.25	
	3
1.5	4.5

2. Write an equation that represents the relationship between *p* and *q*.

3. Summarize how you can write the equation that represents the relationship between two variables that vary directly if you are given a ratio table.

4. Graph your equation. Label your axes.

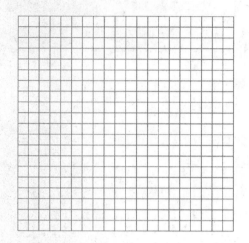

5. Summarize how to draw a graph from the equation representing the relationship between two quantities that vary directly.

6. Summarize how you can write the equation representing the relationship between two quantities that vary directly if you are given a graph.

TALK the TALK

Every Which Way

You have seen how to represent proportional relationships in scenarios, on graphs, in tables, and with equations.

1. Write an equation and sketch a graph to represent each relationship. Label your axes and identify the constant of proportionality on the graph.

   a. Suppose the quantity c varies directly as the quantity d.

   b. Suppose the quantity d varies directly as the quantity c.

2. Write a scenario which describes a proportional relationship between two quantities. Represent this relationship using an equation, a graph, and a table. For each model, identify the constant of proportionality and explain how the model shows that the relationship is proportional.

Scenario

Equation

A PROPORTIONAL RELATIONSHIP

Table

Graph

Assignment

Write

Describe how a table, an equation, and a graph can each represent a direct variation.

Remember

Proportional relationships can be represented in a lot of different ways, including diagrams, tables, equations, graphs, and in scenarios.

Practice

1. The constant of proportionality between the number of children (c) on a field trip and the number of teachers (t) on the trip is $\frac{14}{3}$.
   a. Write an equation to represent this situation.
   b. Create a graph.
   c. If there are 70 children on a field trip. How many teachers are on the trip?

2. The constant of proportionality between the number of junior varsity players (j) on the track team and the number of varsity players (v) on the team is $\frac{2}{5}$.
   a. Write an equation to represent this situation.
   b. Create a graph.
   c. If there are 45 varsity players on the track team. How many junior varsity players are on the team?

3. The constant of proportionality between the number of cats (c) in a pet shelter and the number of dogs (d) in the shelter is 3.
   a. Write an equation to represent this situation.
   b. Create a graph.
   c. If there are 27 cats in the shelter. How many dogs are in the shelter?

4. The constant of proportionality between the height of the water in a sink (h) in centimeters and the number of minutes it has been filling (m) is 0.95. The sink has been filling for 40 minutes. What is the height of the water in the sink?

5. The constant of proportionality between the number of fiction books (f) and the number of nonfiction books (n) in a library is $\frac{15}{22}$. There are 3498 nonfiction books in the library. How many fiction books are in the library?

6. The constant of proportionality between the number of markers (m) and the number of pencils (p) in an art room is $\frac{8}{3}$. There are 304 markers in the art room. How many pencils are in the art room?

Stretch

A map of the United States is drawn such that 1 inch is equal to 600 miles. What is the approximate distance, on the map, between New York and Los Angeles?

Review

1. Suppose the number of pages (p) that Tony can read varies directly with the amount of time (t) in hours he spends reading. Determine the constant of proportionality and describe its meaning.

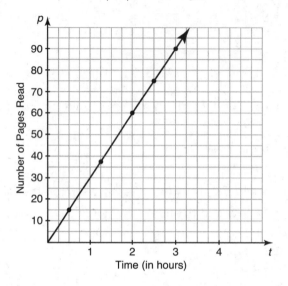

2. In the first quarter (3 months), a store sold 32 limited-edition action figures. If this quarter's sales represent a typical sales pattern, how many action figures should they expect to sell in a year?

3. A recipe calls for $3\frac{1}{2}$ cups of flour and $\frac{3}{4}$ cup of sugar. If you want to make the recipe with 6 cups of flour, how much sugar will you need?

4. Determine the area of each triangle.

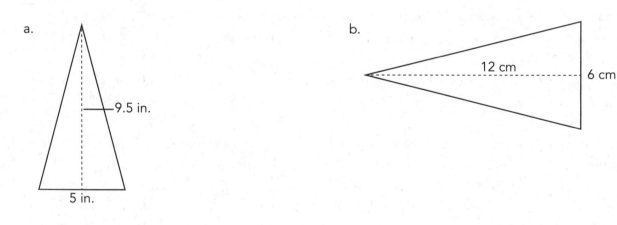

a.

9.5 in.

5 in.

b.

12 cm

6 cm

Proportionality Summary

KEY TERMS

- origin
- proportional relationship

- direct variation
- constant of proportionality

<table>
<tr><td>LESSON
1</td><td>How Does Your Garden Grow?</td></tr>
</table>

One special type of relationship that compares quantities using multiplicative reasoning is a ratio relationship. When two equivalent ratios are set equal to each other, they form a proportion. The quantities in the proportion are in a **proportional relationship**.

For a table of values to represent a proportional relationship, all the ratios of corresponding x- and y-values must be constant.

For example, the table displays the growth rate of a certain species of bamboo by comparing the time in days, x, to the height of the bamboo in centimeters, y. Does the table show a proportional relationship?

Time (days)	Height of Bamboo (cm)
3	210
10.5	735
18	1260
25.5	1785

$$\frac{3}{210} = \frac{1}{70} \qquad \frac{10.5}{735} = \frac{1}{70} \qquad \frac{18}{1260} = \frac{1}{70} \qquad \frac{25.5}{1785} = \frac{1}{70}$$

All the values $\frac{x}{y}$ represent the same constant, $\frac{1}{70}$, so the table shows a proportional relationship.

For a graph to represent a proportional relationship, the points of the graph must form a straight line and pass through the origin. The **origin** is the point with the ordered pair (0, 0).

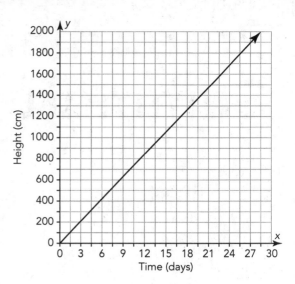

For example, the values from the bamboo situation are graphed here. The graph represents a proportional relationship. It also represents a direct variation. A situation represents a **direct variation** if the ratio between the y-value and its corresponding x-value is constant for every point. The bamboo grows at a constant rate of 70 centimeters a day. The height varies directly as time.

Complying with Title IX

If y is directly proportional to x, the relationship can be represented by the equation $y = kx$, where k is the **constant of proportionality.** This means that for any value of x, the value of y is x multiplied by k.

For example, the table of values represents a proportional relationship. Determine the constant of proportionality.

Girls	Boys
5	6
10	12
15	18

$y = kx$
$6 = k \cdot 5$
$\frac{6}{5} = k$

You can use the constant of proportionality to determine unknown values in proportions.

For example, using the constant of proportionality represented in the previous table, determine how many girls there are if there are 240 boys.

$$\frac{5}{6} = \frac{g}{240}$$
$$(5)(240) = 6g$$
$$1200 = 6g$$
$$200 = g$$

There are 200 girls.

For example, consider the same ratio of 5 girls to 6 boys. If you know the number of boys and need to determine the number of girls, you can use the equation $y = \frac{5}{6}x$. In this equation, the $\frac{5}{6}$ represents the constant of proportionality. For any number of girls, the number of boys is $\frac{5}{6}$ times the number of girls. If you know the number of girls and need to determine the number of boys, you can use the equation $y = \frac{6}{5}x$. In this scenario, the constant of proportionality is $\frac{6}{5}$. You can multiply the number of boys by $\frac{6}{5}$ to determine the number of girls.

<table>
<tr><td>LESSON
3</td><td>**Fish-Inches**</td></tr>
</table>

The constant of proportionality of a situation can be graphed in two different ways.

For example, Stephen walks at a constant rate of 3 miles per hour.

The first graph shown represents the ratio of distance to time. The point (1, 3) represent the unit rate. The ratio $\frac{3}{1}$ represents the constant of proportionality, $k = 3$.

The second graph shown represents the ratio of time to distance.

The point $(1, \frac{1}{3})$ represent the unit rate. The ratio $\frac{\frac{1}{3}}{1}$ represents the constant of proportionality, $k = \frac{1}{3}$.

You can determine the constant of proportionality from a graph.

For example, the third graph shown displays the proportional relationship between the time and distance Melanie walks. Determine the constant of proportionality in miles per hour.

Choose an ordered pair from the graph: (4, 10).

$$k = \frac{y}{x}$$
$$k = \frac{10}{4}$$
$$k = 2.5$$

The constant of proportionality is 2.5.

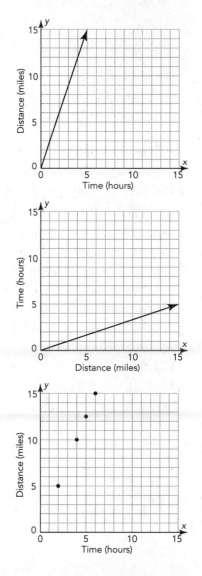

Minding Your Ps and Qs

Proportional relationships can be represented in many different ways, including diagrams, tables, equations, and graphs. They can also be described in scenarios.

A graph can be used to write an equation.

For example, the graph shows Patrick's total number of free throw attempts and the total number of free throws made. The graph represents a proportional relationship because it is a straight line that goes through the origin. Using the graph, you can determine that the constant of proportionality is $k = \frac{4}{7}$, which means that Patrick made $\frac{4}{7}$ of the free throws he attempted. The equation that represents this is $y = \frac{4}{7}x$.

A scenario can also be used to write an equation.

For example, a blue whale eats 8000 pounds of food a day. Let x represent the independent quantity, the number of days, and let y represent the dependent quantity, the number of pounds of food eaten. The constant of proportionality is 8000, meaning that for every day that passes, the amount of food in pounds that the blue whale has eaten increases by 8000. The equation that represents this is $y = 8000x$.

A table of values can be created using an equation.

For example, the equation $y = 8000x$ from the blue whale scenario can be used to create the table of values shown.

Number of Days	Pounds of Food
0	0
1	8000
4	32,000
9	72,000

Proportional Relationships

Did you get good service in a restaurant? If you did, it is common to leave a 20% tip for the server that waited on you.

Lesson 1
Markups and Markdowns
Introducing Proportions to Solve Percent Problems M1-161

Lesson 2
Perks of Work
Calculating Tips, Commissions, and Simple Interest M1-177

Lesson 3
No Taxation Without Calculation
Sales Tax, Income Tax, and Fees M1-197

Lesson 4
More Ups and Downs
Percent Increase and Percent Decrease. M1-209

Lesson 5
Pound for Pound, Inch for Inch
Scale and Scale Drawings M1-223

Module 1: Thinking Proportionally

TOPIC 4: PROPORTIONAL RELATIONSHIPS

In this topic, students use their knowledge of proportionality to solve real-world problems about money and scale drawings. They solve a wide variety of multistep ratio and percent problems, including problems about tax, markups and markdowns, gratuities, simple interest, commissions, and scale factors and drawings. Students use percent models, proportions, and the constant of proportionality to solve markup and markdown problems. In addition to considering scenarios involving money, students calculate percent increase and decrease using geometric objects.

Where have we been?

In grade 6, students used ratio strategies, including models and forming equivalent ratios, to solve percent problems involving determining the whole given a part and the percent. In previous lessons in this course, students learned and practiced solving proportions using means and extremes.

Where are we going?

Students learn financial literacy skills related to taxes and fees, commissions, markups and markdowns, tips, simple interest, and percent increase and decrease, including depreciation. They learn how to use proportional reasoning to estimate, calculate, and judge the reasonableness of results of everyday percent problems they will encounter throughout their lives.

Using a Scale Drawing to Solve Problems

The scale drawing is a blueprint for one floor of a new house. Knowing that the scale is the ratio 3 cm : 10 ft can help you determine the actual dimensions of objects in the scale drawing.

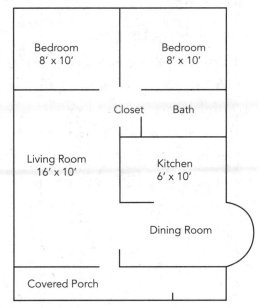

Myth: There is one right way to do math problems.

Employing multiple strategies to arrive at a single, correct solution is important in life. Suppose you are driving in a crowded downtown area. If one road is backed up, then you can always take a different route. If you know only one route, then you're out of luck.

Learning mathematics is no different. There may only be one right answer, but there are often multiple strategies to arrive at that solution. Everyone should get in the habit of saying: Well, that's one way to do it. Is there another way? What are the pros and cons? That way, you avoid falling into the trap of thinking there is only one right way because that strategy might not always work or there might be a more efficient strategy.

Teaching students multiple strategies is important. This helps students understand the benefits of the more efficient method. In addition, everyone has different experiences and preferences. What works for you might not work for someone else.

#mathmythbusted

Talking Points

You can further support your student's learning by asking them to take a step back and think about a different strategy when they are stuck.

Questions to Ask

- What strategy are you using?
- What is another way to solve the problem?
- Can you draw a model?
- Can you come back to this problem after doing some other problems?

Key Terms

percent increase
A percent increase is the ratio of the amount of increase to the original amount, written as a percent.

percent decrease
A percent decrease is the ratio of the amount of decrease to the original amount, written as a percent.

depreciation
Depreciation is decrease in price or value. A car's value depreciates over time.

similar figures
Figures that are proportional in size, or that have proportional dimensions, are called similar figures.

Markups and Markdowns

Introducing Proportions to Solve Percent Problems

1

WARM UP

The regular price of a bathing suit is $89.99. Estimate the sale price of the bathing suit for each of the following sales.

1. 70% off regular price
2. 30% off regular price
3. 50% off regular price
4. 25% off regular price

LEARNING GOALS

- Estimate and calculate the values of percents.
- Use percent models to solve percent problems.
- Use proportional relationships to solve for unknowns in multistep percent problems.
- Solve percent problems using the constant of proportionality.

KEY TERMS

- markdown
- markup

You have used ratio reasoning to solve percent problems. How can you use proportional relationships to solve percent problems involving markdowns and markups?

Need New Kicks?

A marketing department is creating signs for an upcoming shoe sale.

| HOLIDAY SHOE SALE 35% OFF the Regular Price | HOLIDAY SHOE SALE 65% Of Regular Price |

1. Compare the two signs. What do you notice?

2. Which sign should the store use to advertise the shoe sale? Explain your reasoning.

3. The regular price of a pair of shoes is $59.99. Estimate the sale price of the pair of shoes two different ways.

ACTIVITY 1.1

Percent Models

Three percent scenarios are shown. Match each model to the appropriate scenario.

1. A shirt costs $20. If it was on sale for 75% off, what is the discount?

a.
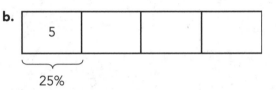

2. A skirt originally cost $28. Alicia pays $21 for the skirt during a sale. What percent does Alicia save with the sale?

b.

5			

25%

3. A ski hat is on sale for 25% off, which is $5 off. What is the original price of the ski hat?

c.
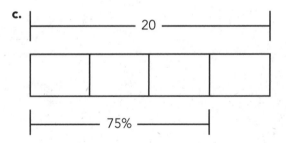

4. Use the appropriate model to solve each percent problem. Explain how you solved each.

5. Keisha said that she had developed strategies to solve percent problems, depending on what was given.

- Case A: If I want to calculate the percent, I can divide the part by the whole and rewrite the decimal as a percent.

- Case B: If I want to calculate the part, or percent of a number, I can multiply the percent, written in decimal form, by the number.

- Case C: If I want to calculate the whole, I can divide the percent, written in decimal form, by the part.

Is Keisha correct?
Does this always work? Explain your thinking.

Corinne, Eduardo, and Adina each set up a proportion to solve four different percent problems.

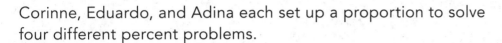

Remember, you can write a percent as a proportion.

$$\frac{\text{part}}{\text{whole}} = \frac{\text{percent number}}{100}$$

1. **Read each percent problem and analyze the corresponding student's work.**

A shirt costs $20. If it is on sale for 75% off, what is the discount?

A skirt originally cost $28. Alicia pays $21 for the skirt during a sale. What percent does Alicia save with the sale?

Corinne 👍

$$\frac{75}{100} = \frac{x}{20}$$

$$(75)(20) = 100x$$

$$1500 = 100x$$

$$\frac{1500}{100} = \frac{100x}{100}$$

$$15 = x$$

The discount is $15.

Eduardo 👍

$$\frac{x}{100} = \frac{21}{28}$$

$$28x = (100)(21)$$

$$28x = 2100$$

$$\frac{28x}{28} = \frac{2100}{28}$$

$$x = 75$$

Alicia paid 75% of the cost, so Alicia saved 25%.

a. **How did Corinne know where to place the 20 in her proportion?**

b. **How did Eduardo decide Alicia saved 25%?**

A ski hat is on sale for 25% off, which is $5 off. What is the original price of the ski hat?

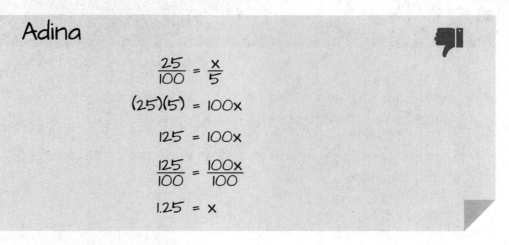

Adina

$$\frac{25}{100} = \frac{x}{5}$$

$$(25)(5) = 100x$$

$$125 = 100x$$

$$\frac{125}{100} = \frac{100x}{100}$$

$$1.25 = x$$

c. **Explain what Adina did incorrectly. Then, set up and solve the problem correctly.**

All of the problems in the previous activity involved a sale or a **markdown**. To make money, businesses often buy products from a wholesaler or distributor for one amount and add to that amount to determine the price they use to sell the product to their customers. This is called a **markup**.

The school store is selling spirit wear. They mark up all of the prices by 20% to sell to the community and students.

2. **If the store's cost for a sweatshirt is $25, what is the customer's cost? Analyze the four student responses shown.**

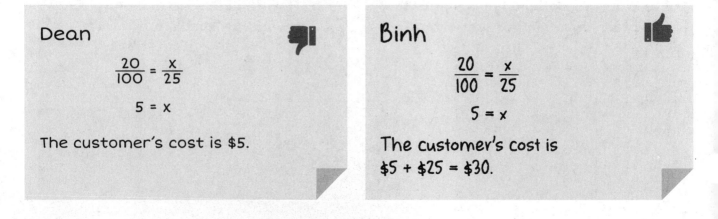

Dean

$$\frac{20}{100} = \frac{x}{25}$$

$$5 = x$$

The customer's cost is $5.

Binh

$$\frac{20}{100} = \frac{x}{25}$$

$$5 = x$$

The customer's cost is $5 + $25 = $30.

Luke

The new "whole" is the total cost, which is 20% more than the original 100%. I can multiply the store cost by 120%, or 1.20.

$$25(1.20) = 30$$

The customer's cost is $30.

Lahari

The original cost is now the part.

$$\frac{100}{120} = \frac{25}{x}$$

$$30 = x$$

The customer's cost is $30.

a. Compare Dean's method to Binh's method.

b. Compare Luke's method to Lahari's method.

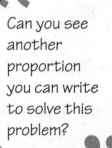

Can you see another proportion you can write to solve this problem?

3. Use the method(s) of your choice to complete the table of the store's cost and the customer's cost for the spirit wear.

	Store's Cost	Customer's Cost
T-shirt	$8	
Face Tattoos		$4.50

Solve each percent problem. Show your work.

4. The $199.99 game console Amy purchased was on sale for 10% off. How much did Amy pay?

5. A computer is normally $899 but is discounted to $799. What percent of the original price does Shawn pay?

You know that the percent whole is always 100. So as long as you know 2 of the other 3 values, you can solve the proportion.

6. If Fernando paid $450 for a netbook that was 75% of the original price, what was the original price?

7. Fantasy-N-Fun sells gaming cards for $9.99 but they pay only $6.75 per card. What is the percent markup?

8. Dontrelle received 30% off when he purchased a rare book regularly priced at $96.50. How much did Dontrelle pay?

9. Brittany is selling car magnets. She purchases them for $7.50 each and marks up the price by 30%. How much is Brittany planning to charge?

Chet is planning his vacation. The flight he selected was $229.99 but he got 20% off because he booked it online through a new travel website. What did he pay?

1. **Explain why Katie's answer is incorrect. Then, determine the correct answer.**

Katie

$$\frac{20}{100} = \frac{x}{229.99}$$

$$(20)(229.99) = 100x$$

$$\frac{4599.8}{100} = \frac{100x}{100}$$

$$45.998 = x$$

So, Chet paid about $46.

2. **Explain why Emma's method worked.**

Emma

$$\frac{80}{100} = \frac{x}{229.99}$$

$$(80)(229.99) = 100x$$

$$\frac{18399.2}{100} = \frac{100x}{100}$$

$$183.99 = x$$

Chet paid $183.99 for his flight.

Solve each problem.

3. Anita sold USB thumb drives for $4.95, which was a 10% markup from what she paid for each. How much did Anita pay for the drives?

4. Games that usually sell for $36.40 are on sale for $27.30. What percent off are they?

5. Jimmy's new cell phone cost him $49.99 when he signed a 2-year plan, which was 75% off the original price. What was the original price?

A rebate is a refund of part of the amount paid for an item. Generally, a customer mails a completed form to the company after a purchase, and a rebate check is mailed to the customer.

6. Liz is shopping for a game system. Two competing stores offer deals on the system that she wants to purchase.

Game Hut	Fun n Games
• $375	• $399
• 15% off sale on all game systems	• $50 rebate after the purchase

Where should Liz shop? Show all of your work and explain your reasoning.

7. Dante has been shopping around for a new mountain bike. He found two bikes that he likes equally—one is sold at Mike's Bikes for $300, and the other is sold at Cycle Center for $275.

Dante has a coupon for 25% off any bike at Mike's Bikes. However, the manufacturer of the bike at Cycle Center has included a $40 rebate after the purchase of the bike.

Where should Dante purchase his mountain bike? Show all of your work and explain your reasoning.

8. Barry is shopping for a new sweater that originally cost $50.00. The department store has all items marked down by 20%. He also has a coupon for an additional 10% off all purchases.

> **Barry**
>
> Since all items are marked down by 20%, and I have an additional 10% off, that means I get a 30% discount.
>
> $$\frac{30}{100} = \frac{X}{50}$$
>
> $$2X = 30$$
>
> $$X = 15$$
>
> The cost of the sweater is $50.00 − $15.00 = $35.00.

Describe Barry's mistake. Then calculate how much Barry will pay for the sweater.

The Shoe Super Store sells name brand shoes at a price much less than most department stores. The chart hanging in the store displays the normal price of the shoes and the Shoe Super Store price.

Regular Department Store Price	Shoe Super Store Price
$20	$16
$25	$20
$30	$24
$35	$28
$40	$32
$50	$40

> Remember, proportions are formed by equivalent ratios.

Alfie

The Shoe Super Store prices do not vary directly with the regular department store prices.

A $20 pair of shoes is only $4 cheaper at the Shoe Super Store, while a $50 pair of shoes is $10 cheaper at Shoe Super Store.

1. Explain what is wrong with Alfie's reasoning.

2. What is the constant of proportionality? Interpret the constant of proportionality for this problem situation.

3. Define the variables and write an equation to represent the relationship between the department store price and Shoe Super Store price.

4. What is the Shoe Super Store price for a pair of shoes that cost $28 at the department store? Explain your reasoning.

5. What is the department store price for a pair of shoes that cost $15 at Shoe Super Store? Explain your reasoning.

TALK the TALK

Percent and Proportions

Demonstrate how to solve any type of percent problem with proportions.

1. Write each proportion, with a variable in the appropriate place, to calculate each specific unknown.

   a. Calculate the Percent

   b. Calculate the Part

   c. Calculate the Whole

Assignment

Write

Explain how to use proportions to solve for the unknown in a percent problem.

Remember

The answer to the percent problem may or may not be the value of the unknown in your proportion. Re-read the problem and ensure that you answer the question being asked.

Practice

1. The cable provider's "triple play" package offers a land line, internet service, and cable TV for one fixed price. If you already subscribe to their cell phone service they offer an additional 12% off the price of the triple play package. If the discounted price of the triple play is $132, what is the price of the package without the discount?

2. The O! Natural Company sells a juice in 1 gallon bottles. The current retail price of the juice is $3.50 for 1 gallon. In order to remain competitive, the company will decrease the price to $3.20.
   a. What percent of the original price are consumers going to pay?
   b. Suppose the company's cost per 1 gallon is $2.70. What is the markup if they sell each gallon at $3.20? What is the markup if they sell each gallon at $3.50?

3. The O! Natural Company is trying to get schools in the state to sell their juice product.
   a. If the sales representative went to 300 schools and convinced 125 to sell their product, what percentage decided to not sell their product? Use two different strategies to calculate the answer.
   b. The sales representative made a deal with the schools for a discount on the individual juice bottles. The company usually sells the bottles to the distributors for $2.25, but they are selling them to the schools for 15% off. For what price will they sell each bottle to the schools?
   c. Suppose the schools pay $2.00 per bottle for the juice and sell it to community members for $2.50 per bottle. What percent markup are they charging?

4. Jillian is shopping for new school supplies. She finds a flyer in the newspaper for her favorite store. They are offering the following coupons.

Office World Sale!	Office World Sale!
All laptops—Buy now and receive a $100 rebate after purchase!	Receive 20% off any one item!
*cannot be used with any other coupons	

   Jillian needs to buy a new laptop for the school year. The list price for the laptop is $479.99. Is it a better deal to use the coupon for the $100 rebate or the 20% off one item? Explain your reasoning.

Stretch

While Emma is shopping with her friend Jacob, they notice a sign in the front of the store.

> **BACK-TO-SCHOOL SALE!**
> - 20% off all purchases
> - $10.00 student discount

They also notice that the two cashiers are applying the discounts differently. The cashier on their left is taking 20% off the total bill and then subtracting $10.00. The cashier on their right is subtracting $10.00 first and then taking 20% off the total.

In order to get a better deal, should Emma and Jacob go to the cashier on the left or the right? Or does it not matter? Show all of your work and explain your reasoning.

Review

1. Millie is cutting out stars to decorate the gym for the school dance. The number of stars (s) she can cut out varies directly with the time (t) in minutes she spends cutting out the stars.

   a. Write an equation to show the relationship between s and t.

   b. Complete the table to show the number of stars Millie is able to cut out for various amounts of time.

Time (t) (in minutes)	Number of Stars (s)	$\frac{s}{t} = k$
	0	......
12	6	
	15	
44		
50		

   c. Write an equation to represent the relationship between s and t using the value of k you determined from the table.

   d. Graph the data. Label the x- and y-axes and title your graph.

   e. Did the graph turn out as you expected? Explain.

   f. Explain how to determine the constant of proportionality using the graph.

2. Determine if there is a proportional relationship between the two quantities. Explain your reasoning.

   a.

A	B
35	92
23	80

   b.

C	D
20	8
12.5	5

3. Determine two equivalent ratios for each ratio given.

   a. $\frac{2}{5}$

   b. 6 yellow : 9 blue

Perks of Work

2

Calculating Tips, Commissions, and Simple Interest

WARM UP

Express each percent as a decimal and as a fraction.

1. 47%

2. 3%

3. 12.5%

4. 0.25%

5. 4.99%

LEARNING GOALS

- Use percent equations to solve for unknowns in multistep percent problems.
- Solve multistep percent problems using direct variation.
- Solve multistep percent problems using the constant of proportionality.

KEY TERMS

- percent equation
- simple interest
- commission

You have used proportions to solve percent problems involving markups and markdowns. How can you use proportions and percent equations to solve for the unknown in different types of percent problems?

Getting Started

Make Sure to Tip Your Servers

> A patron is another word for a person who eats at a restaurant.

Most restaurant patrons add a tip to the final bill to show their appreciation for the wait staff. Usually, a patron will determine 15% to 20% of the bill, and then add that amount to the total. Many times, patrons will just round off the tip to the nearest dollar.

You can use benchmark percents to estimate the amount of any tip. Common benchmark percents used in calculating tips are 1%, 5%, 10%, and 25%.

WORKED EXAMPLE

One strategy to determine a 20% tip for a restaurant bill that is $38.95 is to first determine 10% of the total and then double that amount. Ten percent of $38.95 is $3.90, or approximately $4. So, a 20% tip should be about $8.

For each bill amount, use benchmark percents to estimate a 15% and 20% tip.

	15% Tip	20% Tip
$89.45		
$125.00		
$12.45		

Introduction to Percent Equations

Now that many people own phones with built-in calculators, some calculate the exact tip for their restaurant bill rather than use rounding and benchmark fractions.

Suppose you want to determine the recommended 15% tip on a restaurant bill of $45.00. You can use a proportion to determine the amount of a tip based on the restaurant total.

1. Use a proportion to determine the amount of a tip based on the restaurant total.

You can also use a *percent equation* to determine the tip amount on a restaurant bill. A **percent equation** can be written in the form percent × whole = part, where the percent is often written as a decimal.

WORKED EXAMPLE

$$\text{percent} = \frac{\text{part}}{\text{whole}}$$

percent as decimal	×	whole	=	part
(tip percent)	of	(total bill)	=	amount of the tip

$$\frac{15}{100} \text{ or } 0.15 \times 45 = t$$

$$6.75 = t$$

---

2. Analyze the worked example.

   a. Describe how the percent equation in the form percent × whole = part is equivalent to a proportion in the form percent = $\frac{part}{whole}$.

   b. Explain how the variable is isolated. Then, describe how the tip amount is calculated using the percent equation.

3. Use proportions and percent equations to calculate tips on the given restaurant bills. For each, isolate the variable first. Then, determine the tip amount. Finally, write your answer in a complete sentence.

Bill	Percent	Use a Proportion	Use a Percent Equation
$63.89	20%		
Sentence			
$24.40	15%		
Sentence			

4. Describe how the strategies you used to solve the proportions and the percent equations are similar.

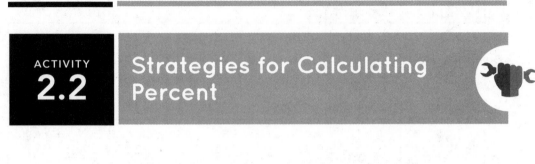

ACTIVITY 2.2

Strategies for Calculating Percent

Restaurant servers are not the only people provided with tips for a job well done.

Skylar is a hair stylist at a salon. Her clients pay their bills at the front desk but give her cash for her tip. She wondered what her typical tip percent was, so she calculated the tip percent received from each client on a specific day.

WORKED EXAMPLE

Skylar's first client of the day spent $150 to have her hair dyed and cut, and gave Skylar a $30 tip.

Use a Proportion	Use a Percent Equation

$$\frac{t}{100} = \frac{30}{150}$$

$$t = \frac{(30)(100)}{150}$$

$$t = 20$$

$$(t)(150) = 30$$
$$150t = 30$$

$$\frac{150t}{150} = \frac{30}{150}$$

$$t = \frac{30}{150}$$

$$t = 0.2$$

---

1. Explain why Skylar's methods result in different values for *t*. What percent tip did Skylar receive from her client?

2. Calculate the tip percent for Skylar's next two clients. Use both proportions and percent equations in the table shown. For each problem, isolate the variable first. Then, calculate the answer. Finally, write your answer in a complete sentence.

Salon Bill	Tip Amount	Use a Proportion	Use a Percent Equation
$80	$15		
Sentence			
$80	$10		
Sentence			

3. Describe the strategies you used to solve each proportion and each percent equation.

Strategies for Calculating the Whole

Tipping for services is not a universal standard, so some business add an automatic gratuity, or tip, onto every bill. Restaurants frequently add an 18% gratuity when the group includes 8 or more people. Some hotels, resorts, and service providers close to tourist areas often add an automatic 18% gratuity to the bill.

1. The esthetician, manicurist, and massage therapist at the Sun and Sand Resort earn an automatic 18% gratuity on their services. Determine the value of the services each must provide in a day to earn the desired gratuity. Show your work, and then write a sentence to explain your answer.

An esthetician is someone who is knowledgeable about skin care, particularly the face.

	Desired Gratuity	Use a Proportion	Use a Percent Equation
Esthetician	$100		
Sentence			
Manicurist	$150		
Sentence			
Massage Therapist	$200		
Sentence			

2. Crystal says that when she solved the proportions in Question 1, she could set up her proportions in any way she wanted because ratios can be written in any way. Do you agree with Crystal's statement? Explain your reasoning.

ACTIVITY 2.4

Tips and Direct Variation

A room service waiter or waitress at a hotel receives an automatic gratuity that varies directly with the amount of the food bill.

1. Suppose a room service waitress at the Sun and Sand Resort receives gratuity represented by the equation $g = 0.15b$, where g represents the gratuity and b represents the food bill.

    a. What percent gratuity does the room service waitress receive? How do you know?

    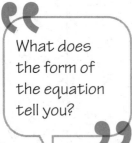

    What does the form of the equation tell you?

    b. If the food bill is $19, how much tip did she receive?

    c. If the room service waitress receives a $2.10 gratuity, how much is the food bill?

2. Write an equation to represent the direct proportional relationship between the amount of gratuity (g) received by a room service waitress and the food bill (b). Let k represent the constant of proportionality. What does the constant of proportionality represent in this equation?

3. Gourmet Eatery has a policy of automatically adding an 18% tip to every restaurant bill.

   a. Write an equation to represent the relationship between the tip (t) and the restaurant bill (b).

   b. How much of a tip is added to a restaurant bill of $54? Use your equation to determine the amount of the tip.

   c. Marie receives a tip of $12. How much is the restaurant bill?

   d. If a restaurant bill is $12, how much is the tip?

   e. How much would a restaurant bill be if it had a tip of $3.20 added to it?

ACTIVITY 2.5

Simple Interest

When you save money in a bank savings account, the bank pays you money each year and adds it to your account. This additional money is interest, and it is added to bank accounts because banks routinely use your money for other financial projects. They then pay interest for the money they borrow from you.

An original amount of money in your account is called the principal. Interest is calculated as a percent of the principal. One type of interest is **simple interest**, which is a fixed percent of the principal. Simple interest is paid over a specific period of time—either twice a year or once a year, for example. The formula for simple interest is:

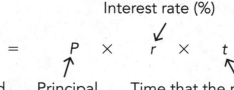

Interest rate (%)

$$I = P \times r \times t$$

Interest earned (dollars) Principal (dollars) Time that the money earns interest (years)

WORKED EXAMPLE

For example, Kim deposits $300 into a savings account at a simple interest rate of 5% per year.

You can use the formula to calculate the interest she will have earned at the end of 3 years.

Interest = Principal $\times$ rate $\times$ time

Interest = (300)(0.05)(3)

$\quad\quad = \$45$

Kim will have earned $45 in interest after 3 years.

---

1. Complete the table by using your knowledge of the formula for simple interest.

Principal Amount Saved (dollars)	Interest Rate	Time (years)	Interest Earned (dollars)
425	7%	5	
75	3%	1	
250	2%	8	
340	5%	2	
	4%	3	30.00
456	6%		109.44
500		4	120.00

In the same way that banks pay you interest when they use your money for financial projects, you too pay interest as well.

2. When you borrow money from a bank, the amount you borrow is the principal, and you pay the interest on that money to the bank. Complete the table shown.

Principal Borrowed (dollars)	Interest Rate	Time (years)	Interest Paid (dollars)
5000	6%	10	
450	5%	2	
1500	7%	3	
	2%	20	7200

ACTIVITY 2.6

Commissions and Proportionality

A **commission** is an amount of money a salesperson earns after selling a product. Many times, the commission is a certain percent of the product.

A car salesperson makes a 10% *commission* on each sale. A salesperson's commission is proportional to the cost of the products sold.

1. **Complete the table to show the relationship between the price of a car and the commission the salesperson receives.**

Price (dollars)	Commission (dollars)
0	
9000	
15,000	
	1000
18,000	
	2000

To help with sales goal-setting, the salesperson wants to create a visual to display in the office.

2. **Graph the relationship between the price of a car and the commission received.**

3. Explain how the graph illustrates that the relationship between car price and commission is proportional.

> Because commission is proportional to the cost of products sold, you can make all kinds of predictions in these situations.

4. Define the variables and write the equation that represents the relationship between the price of a car and the commission received.

5. How much commission will the salesperson earn for selling a $25,000 car? Determine the commission using your equation.

6. If the salesperson earned a $1250 commission, what was the price of the car? Determine the price of the car using your equation.

For each commission situation, define variables for the varying quantities, write a percent equation to represent the relationship, and then answer the question.

7. An automobile saleswoman earns 12% on all of her sales. Last month, she sold 3 cars for a total sales amount of $28,950. What is her commission?

8. A real estate agent earns 6% of the selling price of each house he sells. If he sells a home for $250,000, how much of a commission will he make?

9. If a car salesman made $2450 from a 12% commission on a car sale, what is the cost of the car he sold?

10. A real estate agent made $7500 on a $150,000 home sale. What was the percent of her commission?

TALK the TALK

Where's Bob?

Each of the restaurant receipts shown includes a missing meal total of a guest who paid a specific percent of the total bill. The tip amount for each table is also provided. Use the receipts to answer the questions.

Table 1

Guest 1:

Guest 2: $18.00

Guest 3: $12.00

  Tip: $4.96

Table 2

Guest 1: $38.45

Guest 2: $34.81

Guest 3:

  Tip: $14.65

Table 3

Guest 1: $18.22

Guest 2:

Guest 3: $41.00

  Tip: $11.74

Table 4

Guest 1: $35.11

Guest 2: $35.05

Guest 3:

  Tip: $15.90

1. Bob ate at a restaurant one night with 2 friends. The cost of his meal was 10% of the total food bill but not clearly shown on the receipt. He knows that his group tipped either 15% or 18%, but he's not sure which. At which table did Bob sit and what was the cost of his meal? What percent did his table tip?

2. Assume, instead, that the mystery guest at each table paid 20% of the total bill. Determine the total bill and what percent tip each table gave their waitstaff.

Assignment

Write

Explain how to solve for any unknown with a percent equation.

Remember

When a tip, gratuity, or commission varies directly with the cost of the product, you can represent the situation using the equation $t = kb$, where t represents the amount of tip, gratuity, or commission, k represents the percent of tip, and b represents the total cost of the product.

Practice

1. Ben recently purchased a new home. In order to be able to afford the home, he came up with a budget that breaks down his monthly income as follows: 30% for housing, 20% for food, 22% for utilities, 10% for savings, 6% for entertainment, and 12% for personal items. Ben has a net income of $4000 per month. Calculations for budget are identical to calculations for tips and commissions. Use what you know about computing tips and commissions to answer each question. For each question,
   - set up and solve a proportion,
   - set up and solve a percent equation, and
   - write a sentence to explain your answer.
   a. Calculate the amount of money that Ben will have each month for his most essential budget items: housing, food, and utilities.
   b. Last month Ben spent $380 on food and $420 on personal items. What percent of his monthly income did he spend on these items?
   c. After 5 years, Ben's income has undergone several increases. Last month, Ben put $600 in savings, which was 10% of his net income. What is Ben's new monthly net income?
   d. Ben would like to purchase a new home. He figures out that his monthly housing costs for the new home will be $2100 per month. If he wants to keep the housing costs as 30% of his budget, what will his monthly net income need to be?
2. Joan receives a 4% commission on the merchandise she sells in a department store.
   a. Write an equation to represent the relationship between the total sales (s) and the commission (c) received.
   b. How much commission would Joan receive if the merchandise she sold totaled $139?
   c. How much would Joan have to sell to earn a commission of $100?
3. Serena deposits $1200 into a savings account that earns simple interest. The interest is applied to her account at the end of each year. Complete the table.

Year	Principal Balance	Interest Rate	Interest Earned
1	$1200	2%	
2	$1224	2%	
3		3%	

4. In the community of Greendale, a local restaurant allows student-based clubs to host fundraising nights. The organizations must hand out flyers ahead of time, and the customers who come to dine at the restaurant must present the flyer with their order. The restaurant will donate 15% of the total sales to the organization.

   a. If the sales total $8000, how much will the organization make?

   b. Write an equation to represent the relationship between the dinner sales (d) and the amount (A) the organization will receive.

   c. What is the constant of proportionality? Interpret the constant of proportionality for this problem situation.

   d. What were the total dinner sales if the organization was given $885 by the restaurant? Explain your reasoning.

5. A restaurant also donates a percentage of its total sales for the entire day to a local soup kitchen. The table shows the total sales for different days and the amount that was donated to the soup kitchen.

Total Sales (in dollars)	Amount Donated (in dollars)
10,400	416
14,300	572
15,500	620
18,300	732

   a. What percent of the total sales does the restaurant donate to the soup kitchen? How do you know?

   b. Write an equation to represent the relationship between the total sales (s) and the amount donated to the soup kitchen (d).

   c. What is the constant of proportionality? Interpret the constant of proportionality for this problem situation.

   d. If the restaurant donated $690 to the soup kitchen, what were the total sales for the day?

Stretch

AnnaMarie goes to dinner at a restaurant where the sales tax on meals is 9%. She leaves a tip that is 175% of the amount of sales tax. If her total bill is $45, what was the cost of her meal and what percent tip did she leave?

Review

1. Lyndi has started a home business making and selling all natural goat milk soaps.
   a. If the cost of the materials for a basic bar of soap is $2.50 and Lyndi sells each bar of soap for $4.50, what is the markup percent?
   b. Lyndi sells intricately shaped holiday soaps for $9 each. After each holiday, she marks the related soaps down to $6.75. What percent discount should she advertise on her social media site?

2. Alexander is selling homemade granola to raise money to support having a pet iguana. He makes a batch of granola and then divides it into 14 individual bags for sale. The total cost of the ingredients is $35.
   a. Alexander sells each bag at a markup of 50%. How much does each bag cost? How much money does Alexander make?
   b. If Alexander has not sold all of the granola after 3 days, he sells the remaining bags for 60% of the cost. What is the sale price of the individual bags of granola?

3. Jameer works in a men's clothing store. The amount of money (m) he makes is directly proportional to the number of hours (h) he works.
   a. Complete the table to show the amount of money Jameer earns for different amounts of time that he works.
   b. Determine the constant of proportionality.
   c. Write an equation to show the relationship between m and h.
   d. How many hours does Jameer have to work to make $100?
   e. How much money does Jameer earn if he works 40 hours?

Hours (h)	Money (m) (in dollars)
3	
	56.25
6	75.00
7.5	

4. Determine the volume of the (a) cube and (b) rectangular prism.

   a.
   5.25 cm

   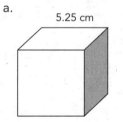

   b.
   6.8 in.

   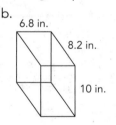

   8.2 in.

   10 in.

No Taxation Without Calculation

Sales Tax, Income Tax, and Fees

WARM UP

Use the Distributive Property to rewrite each product. Then simplify the product. Round to the nearest penny.

1. $7.80(1 + 0.055)

2. $36.41(1 + 0.047)

3. $22(1 + 0.07)

LEARNING GOALS

- Use proportional reasoning to calculate sales tax and income tax amounts.
- Solve sales tax and income tax problems by determining the tax amount, percent, or amount taxed.
- Use proportionality to solve multistep ratio and percent problems involving taxes and fees by writing equations.

KEY TERMS

- sales tax
- income tax

You have used proportionality and percent to solve problems involving price markups and markdowns, tips, and commissions. How can you apply proportional reasoning to solve problems about taxes?

Pay the Piper

If you have ever bought something at the store, you may have noticed that the actual cost of the item ended up being more than what was listed. This is because sales tax is often added to the purchase price. **Sales tax** is a percentage of the selling price of a good or service which is added to the price.

Sales tax percents vary from state to state, though they are usually between 4% and 7%. The percents can also change over time. Sales tax is one of the largest sources of earnings for state governments. Sales taxes fund transportation and public schools.

1. The table shown lists 13 states and the different sales tax added to every dollar of a purchase as of January 2016. Complete the table by determining the tax amount added to each purchase amount. If necessary, round your answer to the nearest penny.

State	Sales Tax (percent)	Tax on $10.00 (dollars)	Tax on $100.00 (dollars)
Indiana	7		
Florida	6		
Arizona	5.6		
Kansas	6.5		
Alabama	4		
Missouri	4.225		
Minnesota	6.875		
Oklahoma	4.5		
Utah	5.95		
Colorado	2.9		
Illinois	6.25		
North Carolina	4.75		
Nebraska	5.5		

ACTIVITY

3.1

Sales Tax

Past sales tax information for California, Maine, and Texas is shown.

California

List Price of an Item ($)	Price Including Sales Tax ($)
12	12.99
30	32.48
117	126.65
200	216.50
250	270.63
369.52	400

Texas

$y = 1.0625x$, where x is the list price and y is the price including sales tax.

Maine

(100, 105)

(10, 10.50)

Price with Sales Tax ($)

List Price ($)

1. Consider the three state tax representations to answer each question.

   a. Determine the cost, including sales tax, of an item which has a list price of $150 for each state. Show all of your work and explain your reasoning.

   b. Determine the list price of an item that cost $200 including sales tax for each state. Show all of your work and explain your reasoning.

c. Which of the three states had the highest sales tax? Explain your reasoning.

d. What was the sales tax percent in each of the three states? Explain your reasoning.

2. Consider the equation for the sales tax in Texas. Why is multiplying the list price by 1.0625 to determine the price including tax the same as calculating the sales tax and then adding it to the list price?

Do you have to calculate the sales tax to determine which state is the highest?

3. The table shows the price of several products and the amount of sales tax added to the price in Pennsylvania.

Cost of Product (dollars)	Sales Tax (dollars)
16	0.96
20	1.20
80	4.80

a. What percent is Pennsylvania's sales tax? How do you know?

b. How much sales tax would there be on a $750 flat screen TV? Show how you determined your answer.

c. If the sales tax on a lawn mower is $48, how much is the cost of the mower?

Income tax is a percent of a person's or company's earnings that is collected by the government. State income tax is defined and applied differently according to the state in which you live. For example, in 2012, New York residents might have paid over 8% of their earnings in state income tax, while residents of Nevada and Texas did not pay state income tax.

> Sales tax and income tax are often called rates. This is because they are ratios of amount taxed per dollar spent or earned.

1. If the income tax rate is 4%, determine the amount of income tax paid on an income of:

   a. $40,000.

   b. $60,000.

   c. $75,000.

2. Write an equation to describe the amount of income tax paid on an income of x dollars if the income tax rate is 4%.

3. Suppose the income tax rate is 6%. Determine the amount of money remaining after paying income tax on an income of:

   a. $50,000.

   b. $80,000.

   c. $95,000.

4. Write an algebraic equation to describe the amount of money remaining after income tax is paid on an income of x dollars if the income tax rate is 6%.

5. Suppose the income tax rate is 5%. Determine a person's income before taxes if the amount of money taken out in taxes is:

   a. $100.

   b. $500.

   c. $2000.

6. Maxine moved out of state and just got her first job, paying $21.50 per hour. She works 40 hours per week and gets paid every 2 weeks. She pays 4% state income tax. How much does Maxine have remaining after state income tax is deducted from her paycheck?

Tori orders yarn online to make hats for her crochet store. Because she orders her materials from out of the country, she pays a total of 20% in fees, including shipping, on each order.

1. Identify the constant of proportionality and interpret its meaning.

2. Complete the table to determine the amounts Tori paid on each of the four orders shown. Then create a graph.

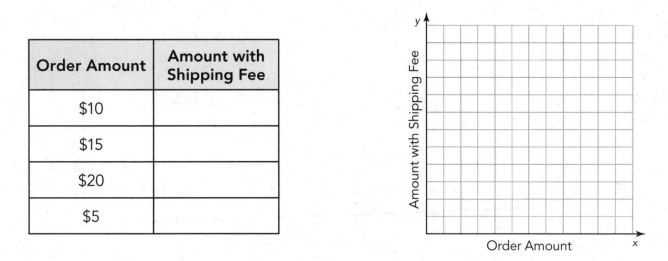

Order Amount	Amount with Shipping Fee
$10	
$15	
$20	
$5	

3. Write an equation to represent the relationship between the order amount and the total amount with shipping fees.

TALK the TALK

Life and Taxes

You have learned about markups and markdowns, tips, discounts, commissions, fees, and taxes.

1. What similarities and differences can you describe about all of these percent relationships?

2. Which of the percent relationships represent an increase from an original amount? Which represent a decrease? Explain your answers.

Assignment

Write

Write a definition for each in your own words. Provide an example for each definition.

1. sales tax
2. income tax

Remember

When calculating the total cost of a good or service that includes sales tax ($x\%$) multiplying the list price by ($1 + x\%$) is the same as adding the sales tax ($x\%$) to the list price.

Practice

1. Three friends live in three different states. Monica lives in Rhode Island, Anthony lives in Ohio, and Thomas lives in Colorado.

Colorado Sales Tax	
List Price ($)	Price Including Sales Tax ($)
3.50	3.60
8.75	9.00
10.99	11.31

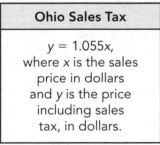

Ohio Sales Tax
$y = 1.055x$, where x is the sales price in dollars and y is the price including sales tax, in dollars.

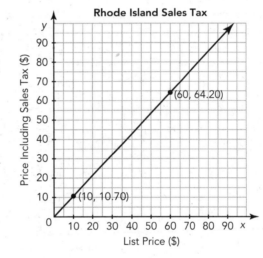

   a. Determine the sales tax rate in each state. Show your work.
   b. All three friends want to purchase the same gaming system so they can play games together. The list price of the gaming system is $349.99. How much will each friend pay for the gaming system?

2. Jesse earned a total of $75,000 this year. He lives in the District of Columbia where the local income tax rate is 8.5% for all incomes over $40,000.
   a. How much will Jesse pay in income tax?
   b. How much money will Jesse have after paying his income tax?

Stretch

In 2015, a person working in the United States paid 10% income tax for income up to $9225. Income between $9226 and $37,450 was taxed at 15%. Suppose John earns $9225. How much of his earnings does John take home after taxes? If he were to get a raise, and John's entire check was taxed at 15%, how much more would he need to earn to take home more than his current take-home pay?

Review

1. Determine each total cost, including a 20% tip, for the following bill amounts. Round to the nearest penny.
   a. $45.80
   b. $103.65

2. The graph shows how many centimeters a bamboo plant can grow and the number of hours that the plant has been growing. Determine the constant of proportionality and explain what it means.

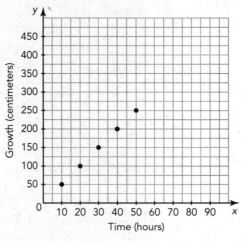

3. In the middle school and high school jazz bands, the number of girls is proportional to the total members. Write a constant of proportionality for this situation and explain what it means.

Jazz Band	Number of Girls	Total Members
Middle School	6	15
High School	8	20

4. Write each as a unit rate.
   a. $180 in 5 hours
   b. $1 in tax for $20 spent

More Ups and Downs

4

Percent Increase and Percent Decrease

WARM UP

Determine each product, rounding to the nearest penny. Describe whether the product represents an increase or decrease.

1. $\$450 \times 1.5 = y$

2. $y = \$36 \times 0.9$

3. $\$100 \times 1.1 = y$

4. $\$250 \times 0.99 = y$

LEARNING GOALS

- Calculate a percent increase and decrease.
- Calculate the depreciation in a value.
- Use proportional reasoning to solve multistep problems involving percent increases and decreases.
- Use proportional reasoning to solve multistep problems involving area, volume, and surface area of two- and three-dimensional objects.

KEY TERMS

- percent increase
- percent decrease
- appreciation
- depreciation

You have used proportional reasoning to solve percent problems, including determining markups and markdowns. How can you apply what you know to determine the percent a value has increased or decreased?

Up or Down?

Tell whether each situation represents an increase or a decrease in spending.

1. A $20 shirt is on sale for $16.

2. The cost of a movie ticket in the afternoon is $6.50, and it is $8.00 after 5:00 p.m.

3. A ride-all-day amusement park ticket last season was $27, and this season it is $35.

4. The cost of lunch yesterday was $5.50, and the cost of lunch today is $5.25.

ACTIVITY 4.1

Percent Increase and Decrease

You have used percents in many different situations. You can also use percents to describe a change in quantities.

A **percent increase** occurs when the new amount is greater than the original amount, such as when stores mark up the price they pay for an item to make a greater profit.

1. All That Glitters Jewelry Store marks up its prices so it can maximize its profits. What is the percent increase for each item? Use the formula shown to complete the table.

$$\text{Percent Increase} = \frac{\text{Amount of Increase}}{\text{Original Amount}}$$

All That Glitters Accounting Sheet				
Item	Cost (dollars)	Customer's Price (dollars)	Difference (dollars)	Percent Increase
Initial ring	60	90		
ID bracelet	120	240		
Earrings	25	50		
Pin	36	45		

A **percent decrease** occurs when the new amount is less than the original amount. An example of a percent decrease is the amount water evaporates over time. Water evaporates at different rates, depending on the size and shape of the container it is in and the air temperature.

Evaporation is the process by which a liquid changes into a gas or vapor.

2. A science class is conducting an experiment to determine how fast water evaporates. They fill 4 differently shaped containers with water and measure the level once at the beginning of the experiment and once at the end. Use the formula shown to complete the table.

$$\text{Percent Decrease} = \frac{\text{Amount of Decrease}}{\text{Original Amount}}$$

Container	Starting Height (cm)	Ending Height (cm)	Difference (cm)	Percent Decrease
A	7.1	4.5		
B	2.3	0.9		
C	3.8	2.9		
D	9.2	7.6		

3. How do you know if the percent is a decrease or increase?

Sometimes people incorrectly use "200% increase" to mean a 100% increase.

4. How would you describe a 50 percent decrease?

5. How would you describe a 100 percent increase?

6. Jake was doing a great job at work, so his boss gave him a 20 percent raise. But then he started coming to work late and missing days, so his boss gave him a 20 percent pay cut. Jake said, "That's okay. At least I'm back to where I started."

Is Jake correct in thinking he is making the same amount of money when he received a pay cut? If you agree, explain why he is correct. If you do not agree, explain to Jake what is incorrect with his thinking and determine what percent of his original salary he is making now.

7. Analyze each student's percent reasoning.

Brett 👎
If you multiply a number n by 0.5, that's a 50% increase, because 0.5 = 50%.

Brendon 👍
If you multiply a number n by 1.2, that's a 20% increase:
$$n \times 1.2 = n(1 + 0.2)$$
$$= n + 0.2n$$
The expression n + 0.2n means a 20% increase from n.

Martina 👍
If you multiply a number n by 0.9, that's a 10% decrease:
$$n \times 0.9 = n(1 - 0.1)$$
$$= n - 0.1n$$
The expression n - 0.1n means a 10% decrease from n.

Explain what Brett did incorrectly. What expression correctly represents a 50% increase over a number n?

8. Use Brendon's and Martina's methods to determine each percent increase or decrease.

a. A ticket originally cost $20, but its price decreases by 20%.

b. Shawna is making $12 per hour. She gets a 6% increase in pay.

c. This month's rainfall is 30% less than last month's total of 3.5 inches.

d. Yvette's family home is 1600 square feet. They hope to increase the area by 10%.

Generally, things like homes and savings accounts gain value, or appreciate over time. Other things, like cars, depreciate every year. New cars depreciate about 12% of their value each year.

Appreciation is an increase in price or value.

Depreciation is a decrease in price or value.

1. How much would a new car depreciate the first year if it costs:

   a. $35,000?

   b. $45,000?

   c. $20,000?

2. If a car lost $3600 in depreciation in the first year, what is the original cost of this car?

3. Complete the table to record the value of a car that costs $50,000 and depreciates at the rate of 12% per year for the first five years.

Time (years)	Value of the Car (dollars)
0	50,000
1	
2	
3	
4	
5	

4. Complete the graph.

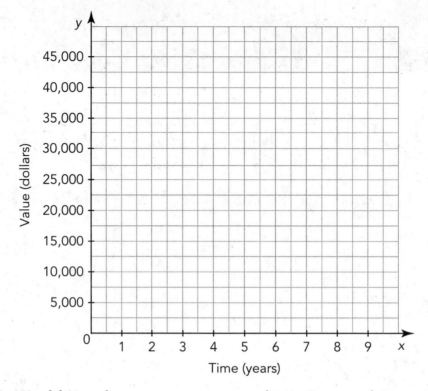

5. Would it make sense to connect the points on the graph? If so, connect the points. Explain your reasoning.

6. Describe how the value of the car decreases over time.

7. Is the relationship between time and the car's value proportional? Explain how you know using the graph and the completed table of values.

ACTIVITY 4.3 Percent Increase and Decrease with Geometry

It is common to talk about percent increases and percent decreases when talking about money. But you can also use them when thinking geometrically.

1. Consider the cubes shown. The side lengths of Cube B are each 20% greater than the side lengths of Cube A.

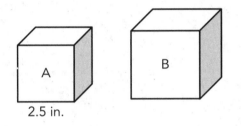

2.5 in.

a. Determine the surface area of each cube. Show your work.

b. Determine the volume of each cube. Show your work.

2. What is the percent decrease in the amount of pizza, from the extra large to the large? Round to the nearest percent. Explain how you determined your answer.

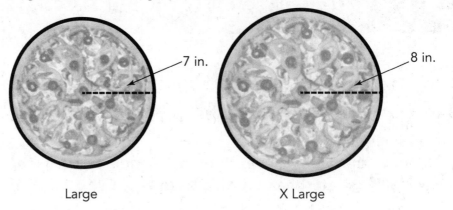

Large   X Large

3. Elinor wanted to order an 18-inch hoagie, which cost $7.99. The sandwich shop is out of 18-inch buns. They only have 12-inch buns.

a. What should be the percent decrease in cost of the hoagie?

b. What should the new cost be?

TALK the TALK

Gas Prices

The table shows the average price of gasoline per gallon in the U.S. for the years 2000 through 2015.

Year	Price ($ per gallon)	% Increase or Decrease
2000	2.02	
2001	1.91	
2002	1.75	
2003	2.01	
2004	2.32	
2005	2.74	
2006	3.00	
2007	3.16	
2008	3.61	
2009	2.58	
2010	3.02	
2011	3.75	
2012	3.80	
2013	3.62	
2014	3.40	
2015	2.45	

1. Complete the table by determining each yearly percent increase or decrease in the price of gasoline. Round to the nearest percent.

2. Casey added together all of the increases from 2000 to 2005 and subtracted the decreases. She concluded that there was about a 35% increase in gas price from 2000 to 2005. Is Casey correct? Explain why or why not.

Assignment

Write

Write a definition for *depreciation* in your own words. Use an example in your definition.

Remember

A percent increase is calculated as a ratio of the amount of increase to the original amount.

A percent decrease is calculated as a ratio of the amount of decrease to the original amount.

Practice

Calculate each percent increase or percent decrease. Round to the nearest whole percent if necessary.

1. original amount: 30, new amount: 45
2. original amount: 12, new amount: 16
3. original amount: 17, new amount: 21
4. original amount: 85, new amount: 56
5. original amount: 48, new amount: 37
6. original amount: 124, new amount: 76

Use the given information to answer each question.

7. A dress that normally sells for $72 is on sale for $45. What is the percent decrease in the price?
8. A home purchased for $120,000 in 2012 is sold for $156,000 in 2015. What is the percent increase in the price?
9. The CD Warehouse purchases CDs for $6 each and sells them for $9 each. What is the percent increase in the price?
10. The CD Warehouse is having a clearance sale. A CD player that originally sells for $60 is now priced at $36. What is the percent decrease in the price?
11. The local high school sold 1914 tickets this year to its spring musical. That was 174 more tickets sold than last year. What is the percent increase in the number of tickets sold?
12. Ken's heart rate went from 74 beats per minute while resting to 148 beats per minute while exercising. What is the percent increase in his heart rate?

Stretch

Can you write a percent decrease as a negative ratio? Provide an example of a percent decrease written as a negative ratio and describe what it means in context.

Review

1. A T-shirt that costs $14 without tax costs $14.98 with tax. What is the sales tax percent?

2. A car that costs $14,000 without tax costs $14,700 with tax. What is the sales tax percent?

3. Identify the constant of proportionality in each situation.

   a. The temperature rises 4 degrees each hour for 10 hours.

   b. Two thirds of the floats in the parade have flowers.

4. Rewrite each algebraic expression with fewer terms.

   a. $9.5(a + 4) - a$

   b. $8 + h - 2 \times 5$

Pound for Pound, Inch for Inch

Scale and Scale Drawings

5

WARM UP

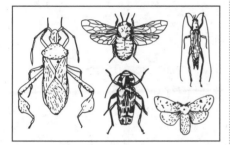

1. These bugs are not drawn to scale. What does that mean?

2. Is it possible that the leftmost bug is the smallest bug in real life? Explain your reasoning.

LEARNING GOALS

- Identify the scale of a drawing as the ratio of drawing length to actual length.
- Compute actual lengths and areas given a scale and a scale drawing.
- Reproduce a scale drawing at a different scale.
- Use concepts of proportionality to determine the scale factor used to produce a scale drawing.

KEY TERMS

- corresponding
- scale
- scale factor
- scale drawing
- similar figures

You have learned a lot about proportional relationships. You can use proportionality to solve problems with geometric figures too. How can you use proportions to investigate real-world and mathematical objects at different scales?

Triangle Drawings

The triangle given, Triangle *A*, is an equilateral triangle—all of its sides are the same length. Each side has a length of 4 units.

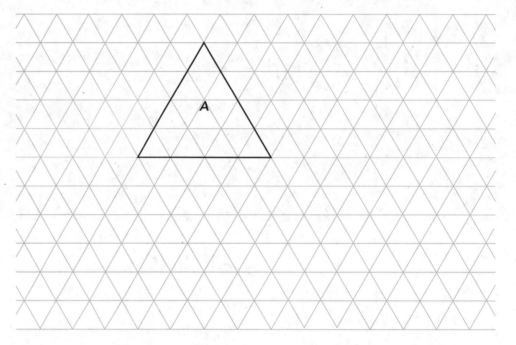

1. Draw a new triangle, Triangle *B*, which has side lengths that are 50% the length of Triangle *A*'s side lengths.

2. Write each ratio to compare Triangle *B* to Triangle *A* in fraction form and as a percent. Describe the meaning of each ratio.

   a. Determine the ratio of corresponding side lengths for each side of the triangles.

   The bottom side of the original triangle and the bottom side of the new triangle are **corresponding** sides.

   b. Determine the ratio of the triangle perimeters.

Scales, Scale Factors, and Scale Drawings

A **scale** is a ratio that compares two measures. The ratios that you wrote to compare the measures of the triangles are scales.

When you multiply a measure by a scale to produce a reduced or enlarged measure, the scale is called a **scale factor**. You can multiply each of Triangle *A*'s lengths by the scale factor 1 : 2, or 50%, or $\frac{1}{2}$, to produce the side lengths for Triangle *B*.

WORKED EXAMPLE

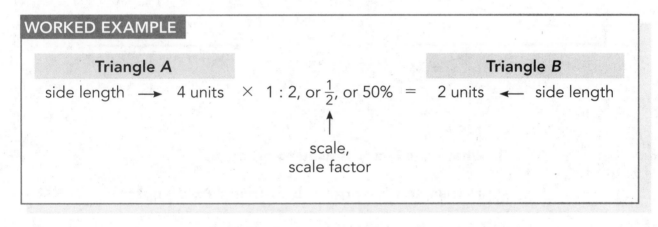

Triangle *A*		Triangle *B*
side length ⟶ 4 units × 1 : 2, or $\frac{1}{2}$, or 50% =	2 units ⟵ side length

↑
scale,
scale factor

1. **What scale factor is used to produce Triangle *A*'s lengths, given Triangle *B*'s lengths? Explain your reasoning.**

Triangle *A*'s side lengths are 200% of Triangle *B*'s side lengths. But they are 100% larger.

2. Draw a triangle, Triangle *C*, whose side lengths are 150% of Triangle *B*'s side lengths.

3. What scale factor is used to produce:

   a. Triangle *C*'s lengths given Triangle *B*'s lengths?

   b. Triangle *B*'s lengths given Triangle *C*'s lengths?

   c. Triangle *C*'s lengths given Triangle *A*'s lengths?

4. Compare the perimeters of Triangles *A*, *B*, and *C*. How did the scale factors affect the perimeters? Explain your reasoning.

A **scale drawing** is a representation of a real object or place that is in proportion to the real object or place it represents. The purpose of a scale drawing is to represent either a very large or very small object. The scales on scale drawings often use different units of measure.

WORKED EXAMPLE

The scale of a drawing might be written as:

1 cm : 4 ft

Drawing   Actual
Length   Length

This scale means that every 1 centimeter of length in the drawing represents 4 feet of the length of the actual object.

The scale of a map might look like this:

1 in. : 200 mi

Map   Actual
Distance   Distance

This scale means that every 1 inch of distance on the map represents 200 miles of actual distance.

---

5. Study the worked example. What scale factor is used to produce:

a. the drawing length given the actual length?

b. the map distance given the actual distance?

6. Write a sentence to describe the meaning of each.

   a. A scale on a map is 1 in. : 2 mi.

   b. A scale on a drawing is 1 cm : 4 cm.

   c. A scale on a drawing is 2 in. : 1 in.

   d. A scale on a drawing is 1 cm : 1 cm.

7. The scale factor for a model car is 1 : 24. What does this mean?

8. The scale factor for a model train is 1 : 87. What does this mean?

Creating Scale Drawings

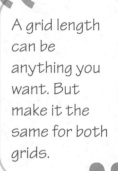

In this activity you will reproduce two different scale drawings at a different scale.

1. The rectangle shown is drawn at a scale of 1 in. : 2 ft.

1 in. : 2 ft

1 in. : 3 ft

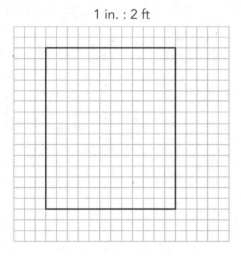

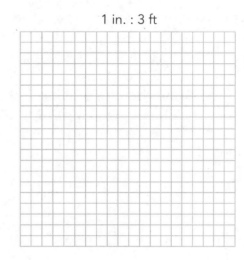

> A grid length can be anything you want. But make it the same for both grids.

a. Draw the rectangle using a scale of 1 in. : 3 ft. Explain your solution.

b. Did you enlarge the rectangle or reduce the rectangle?

c. Show how to calculate the actual dimensions of the rectangle using each scale.

2. The circle shown is drawn at a scale of 2 cm : 3 mi.

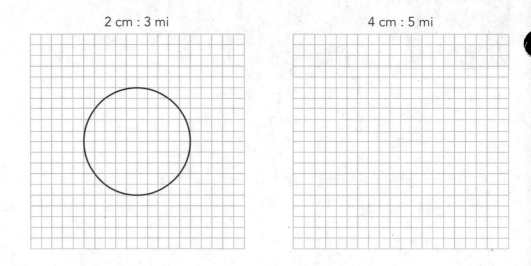

2 cm : 3 mi   4 cm : 5 mi

a. Draw the circle using a scale of 4 cm : 5 mi.
   Explain your solution.

b. Did you enlarge the circle or reduce the circle?

c. Show how to calculate the actual diameter of the circle
   using each scale.

Similar Figures

Figures that are proportional in size, or that have proportional dimensions, are called **similar figures**.

When Timmons Photo Company prints photo packages, they include several sizes of photos that are all mathematically similar. The largest size is 12 in. × 16 in. This is read as "12 inches by 16 inches." The first measure is the width of the photo, and the second measure is the height of the photo.

16 in.

12 in.

Fran and Joe determined the width of a mathematically similar photo that has a height of 8 inches.

Fran 👍

To determine the unknown width of the smaller photo, I wrote ratios using the measurements from within each photo. The ratio on the left contains the measurements of the large photo. The ratio on the right contains the measurements of the smaller photo.

$$\frac{\text{width of larger photo}}{\text{height of larger photo}}$$

$$= \frac{\text{width of smaller photo}}{\text{height of smaller photo}}$$

$$\frac{12 \text{ inches}}{16 \text{ inches}} = \frac{x \text{ inches}}{8 \text{ inches}}$$

$$(12)(8) = (16)(x)$$

$$96 = 16x$$

$$6 = x$$

I calculated that the width of the smaller photo is 6 inches.

Joe 👍

To determine the unknown width of the smaller photo, I wrote ratios using the measurements between the two photos. The ratio on the left contains the width measurements of both photos. The ratio on the right contains the height measurements of both photos.

$$\frac{\text{width of larger photo}}{\text{width of smaller photo}}$$

$$= \frac{\text{height of larger photo}}{\text{height of smaller photo}}$$

$$\frac{12 \text{ inches}}{x \text{ inches}} = \frac{16 \text{ inches}}{8 \text{ inches}}$$

$$(12)(8) = (x)(16)$$

$$96 = 16x$$

$$6 = x$$

I calculated that the width of the smaller photo is 6 inches.

1. **What is similar about the two solution methods? What is different about the two solution methods?**

2. **Determine other possible photo sizes that are mathematically similar.**

    a. 2 in. × _____

    b. 3 in. × _____

    c. _____ × 2 in.

    d. 4 in. × _____

    e. _____ × 3.5 in.

A map of the United States is shown. A scale is included on the map.

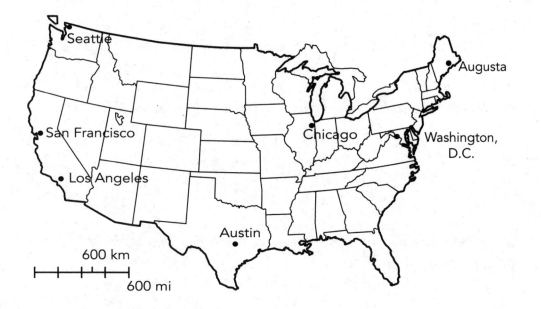

Determine the approximate distances between the locations.
Write the distances in miles and kilometers.

1. Washington, D.C., to San Francisco, California

2. Washington, D.C., to Seattle, Washington

3. Washington, D.C., to your state capital _____

4. Chicago, Illinois, to Los Angeles, California

5. Augusta, Maine, to Austin, Texas

6. Which is longer, a mile or a kilometer? How can you tell?

7. How many kilometers make one mile? Explain how you determined your answer.

8. How many days would it take to travel from Washington, D.C., to San Francisco, California, traveling at 60 miles per hour for 8 hours per day? Show your work.

9. Does your response to Question 8 seem realistic? Explain your reasoning.

Calculating the Scale for a Blueprint

A blueprint is an example of a scale drawing that represents a larger structure. The blueprint shown represents a plan for a new house.

> In blueprints, the ' symbol stands for feet. The " symbol is used for inches.

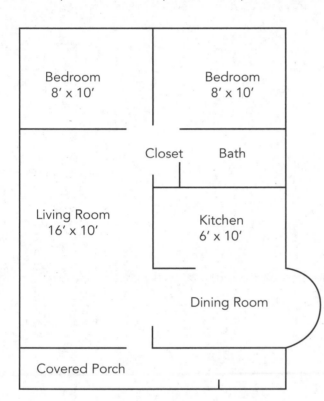

1. **Use a centimeter ruler to determine the scale factor used to create the blueprint. Show your work.**

2. Explain why Marty's reasoning is incorrect. Then, determine the actual area of the covered porch.

> ## Marty 👎
>
> The covered porch measures approximately 2.8 cm by 6 cm.
>
> $2.8 \times 6 = 16.8 \text{ cm}^2$
>
> $16.8 \times \frac{10}{3} = 56$, so the actual area of the covered porch is 56 ft².

3. Determine the approximate area of the dining room. Show your work.

TALK the TALK

Interpreting Scales

1. Which scale would produce the largest scale drawing of an object when compared to the actual object? Explain your reasoning.

   1 in. : 25 in.

   1 cm : 1 m

   1 in. : 1 ft

2. Which scale would produce the smallest scale drawing of an object when compared to the actual object? Explain your reasoning.

   1 in. : 10 in.

   1 cm : 10 cm

   1 mm : 1 m

3. The scale of a drawing is 6 cm : 1 mm. Is the scale drawing larger or smaller than the actual object or place? Explain your reasoning.

4. Given a scale of $\frac{5}{4}$, explain how you can tell whether the drawing is bigger or smaller than the actual object.

Assignment

Write

Write the term that best completes each sentence.

1. The purpose of a(n) _____ is to create an accurate drawing of either a very large or very small object.
2. Two geometric figures that are proportional in size are _____ figures.
3. The "bottom" sides of two similar triangles are _____ sides.

Practice

1. Brent and Margaret are planning a trip to the city of Chicago. The map shown includes several destinations they would like to visit while they are there. A scale is included on the map.

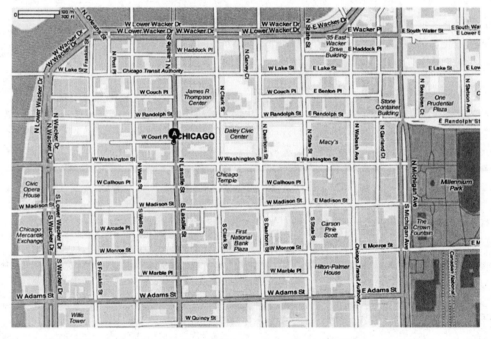

   a. According to the map, which is longer, a meter or a foot? How can you tell?
   b. By following the shortest route along the roads, determine the distance from the Civic Opera House to the Chicago Temple. Write your answer in meters and in feet.
   c. Use the distances you approximated from the Opera House to the Temple to determine the approximate number of feet that are in one meter. Explain your answer.
   d. By following the shortest route along the roads, determine the distance from the Crown Fountain to the James R. Thompson Center. Write your answer in meters and in feet.
   e. By following the shortest route along the roads, determine the distance from the Chicago Mercantile Exchange to Macy's. Write your answer in meters and in feet.

f. Use the distances you approximated from the Chicago Mercantile Exchange to Macy's to determine the approximate number of meters that are in one foot. Explain your answer.

2. While in Chicago, Brent and Margaret plan on visiting the Willis Tower, built as and still commonly referred to as the Sears Tower.

a. In the lobby, there is a model of the Sears Tower that has an observation deck with a height of 4 meters. If the actual height of the observation deck is 412 meters, what is the scale of the model?

b. Brent and Margaret decide to buy a toy replica of the Sears Tower in the gift shop to take home to their neighbors. The toy replica has a scale of 1 inch : 200 feet. Is this replica larger or smaller than the model in the lobby?

c. If the toy replica from the gift shop is 7.25 inches tall, what is the height in feet of the actual Sears Tower? Show your work.

Stretch

You may have seen the star Betelgeuse (BEETLE juice) in the night sky. It is a red giant star, which has a radius of 821.3 million kilometers. By comparison, our Sun has a radius of 0.5 million kilometers.

Suppose the circle shown represents our Sun. How big would the model of Betelgeuse be if you drew it to scale?

Review

1. Determine each percent increase or decrease.

a. Original: $340 New: $34   b. Original: 75 New: 225

2. Solve each proportion.

a. $\frac{4}{x} = 9$ b. $\frac{7.5}{26} = \frac{75}{P}$

3. Graph each inequality on a number line.

a. $x > 7$ b. $-12 \leq x$

Proportional Relationships Summary

KEY TERMS

- markdown
- markup
- percent equation
- simple interest
- commission
- sales tax

- income tax
- percent increase
- percent decrease
- appreciation
- depreciation

- corresponding
- scale
- scale factor
- scale drawing
- similar figures

LESSON 1   Markups and Markdowns

A percent scenario can be represented by a model.

For example, suppose a dress originally cost $36. Annika pays $27 for the dress during a sale. What percent does Annika save with the sale?

The model represents the scenario and can be used to solve the problem. The amount Annika saves is one-fourth the total amount of the dress, so she saves 25%.

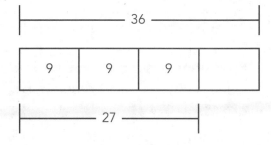

You can write a percent as a proportion.

For example, using the same scenario above, you can set up the proportion $\frac{\text{part}}{\text{whole}} = \frac{\text{percent number}}{100}$.

$$\frac{x}{100} = \frac{27}{36}$$

$$36x = (100)(27)$$

$$\frac{36x}{36} = \frac{2700}{36}$$

$$x = 75$$

Annika paid 75% of the cost, so she saved 25%.

When businesses sell an item at lower price than the original price, the reduction in price is called a **markdown**. To make money, businesses often buy products from a wholesaler or distributor for one amount and add to that amount to determine the price they use to sell the product to their customers. This increase in price is called a **markup**.

For example, a store marks up all of its prices by 25% to sell to its customers. If the store's cost for an item is $16, what is the customer's cost?

$$\frac{25}{100} = \frac{x}{16}$$

$$x = 4$$

The customer's cost is $16 + $4 = $20.

The answer to the percent problem may or may not be the value of the unknown in your proportion. Re-read the problem and ensure that you answer the question being asked.

<table>
<tr><td>LESSON
2</td><td>Perks of Work</td></tr>
</table>

You can use a percent equation to determine the percent of a whole. A **percent equation** can be written in the form percent × whole = part, where the percent is often written as a decimal.

For example, suppose you want to leave a 15% tip on a restaurant bill of $45.

The amount of tip you should leave is $6.75.

		percent	=	$\frac{\text{part}}{\text{whole}}$	
percent	×	whole	=	part	
(tip percent)	of	(total bill)	=	amount of tip	
$\frac{15}{100}$ or 0.15	×	45	=	t	
		6.75	=	t	

Simple interest is a fixed percent of an original amount of money called the principal. The formula for simple interest is:

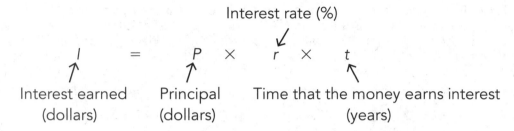

Interest rate (%)

$$I = P \times r \times t$$

Interest earned (dollars)   Principal (dollars)   Time that the money earns interest (years)

A **commission** is an amount of money a salesperson earns after selling a product. Many times, the commission is a certain percent of the product.

For example, a car salesperson's commission varies directly with the cost of the products sold. Determine the percent commission the salesperson makes.

In this scenario, the constant of proportionality is equal to the percent commission, and $k = \frac{700}{7000} = 0.1$. The salesperson makes 10% commission.

Price (dollars)	Commission (dollars)
0	0
7000	700
12,000	1200
23,000	2300

When a tip, gratuity, or commission varies directly with the cost of the product, you can represent the situation using the equation $t = kb$, where t represents the amount of tip, gratuity, or commission, k represents the percent, and b represents the total cost of the product.

LESSON
3

No Taxation Without Calculation

A percent relationship can represent an increase or decrease from an original amount.

Sales tax is a percent of the selling price of a good or service that is added to the price. When calculating the total cost of a good or service that includes sales tax ($x\%$), multiplying the list price by $(1 + x\%)$ is the same as adding the sales tax ($x\%$) to the list price.

Income tax is a percent of a person's or company's earnings that is collected by the government. When calculating the total income after income tax ($x\%$) is taken out, multiplying the income by $(1 - x\%)$ is the same as subtracting the income tax ($x\%$) from the income.

Sales Tax	Income Tax
Rick wants to buy a pair of shoes for $60. The sales tax in his state is 6%. What is the total price Rick will pay for the shoes, including sales tax?	Gia earned an income of $40,000 this year. The income tax rate in her state is 5%. How much will Gia keep after income tax is taken out?
Multiply the list price by $(1 + 0.06)$. $\$60 \times 1.06 = \$63.60$	Multiply the income by $(1 - x\%)$. $\$40,000 \times 0.95 = \$38,000$
Rick will pay $63.60 in total.	Gia will keep $38,000.

LESSON

4

More Ups and Downs

A **percent increase** occurs when the new amount is greater than the original amount, such as when stores mark up the price they pay for an item to make a greater profit. A percent increase is calculated as a ratio of the amount of increase to the original amount.

For example, if you multiply a whole amount n by 1.2, that is a 20% increase.

$n \times 1.2 = n(1 + 0.2) = n + 0.2n$

The expression $n + 0.2n$ means a 20% increase from n.

A **percent decrease** occurs when the new amount is less than the original amount. A percent decrease is calculated as a ratio of the amount of decrease to the original amount.

For example, if you multiply a whole amount n by 0.9, that is a 10% decrease.

$n \times 0.9 = n(1 - 0.1) = n - 0.1n$

The expression $n - 0.1n$ means a 10% decrease from n.

Generally, things such as homes and savings accounts gain value, or appreciate, over time. **Appreciation** is an increase in price or value. Other things, such as cars, depreciate every year. **Depreciation** is a decrease in price or value.

You can use percent increases and decreases when thinking geometrically.

For example, what is the percent decrease in the area from Circle A to Circle B?

The area of Circle A = 36π square units.

The area of Circle B = 16π square units.

$36\pi - 16\pi = 20\pi$

$\frac{20\pi}{36\pi} \approx 0.56$

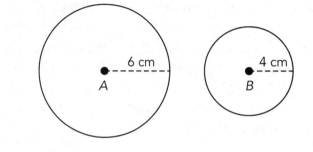

The percent decrease in the area is about 56%.

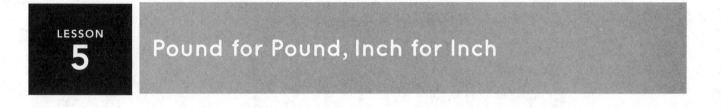

LESSON 5

Pound for Pound, Inch for Inch

A **scale** is a ratio that compares two measures. When you multiply a measure by a scale to produce a reduced or enlarged measure, the scale is called a **scale factor**.

For example, Triangle A is an equilateral triangle with side lengths of 4 units. If Triangle A is reduced by 50% to create Triangle B, what will be the side lengths of Triangle B? You can multiply each of Triangle A's lengths by the scale factor 1 : 2, or 50%, or $\frac{1}{2}$, to produce the side lengths for Triangle B.

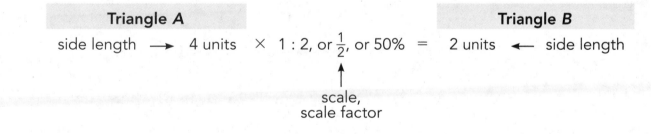

Triangle A			Triangle B
side length ⟶ 4 units	× 1 : 2, or $\frac{1}{2}$, or 50%	=	2 units ⟵ side length

scale,
scale factor

If you draw Triangle A and Triangle B, the bottom sides of the triangles are **corresponding** sides.

A **scale drawing** is a representation of a real object or place that is in proportion to the real object or place it represents. The scales on scale drawings often use different units of measure.

For example, the scale of a drawing might be written: 1 cm : 4 ft. This scale means that every 1 centimeter of length in the drawing represents 4 feet of length of the actual object or place. The scale of a map might be written: 1 in. : 200 mi. This scale means that every 1 inch of distance on the map represents 200 miles of actual distance.

Figures that are proportional in size, or that have proportional dimensions, are called **similar figures**.

For example, a rectangle has a height of 20 inches and a width of 15 inches. Determine the width of a mathematically similar rectangle that has a height of 16 inches.

$$\frac{\text{height of larger rectangle}}{\text{height of smaller rectangle}} = \frac{\text{width of larger rectangle}}{\text{width of smaller rectangle}}$$

$$\frac{20 \text{ inches}}{16 \text{ inches}} = \frac{15 \text{ inches}}{x \text{ inches}}$$

$$(20)(x) = (15)(16)$$

$$20x = 240$$

$$x = 12$$

The width of the similar rectangle is 12 inches.

MODULE 2

OPERATING SIGNED WITH NUMBERS

The lessons in this module build on your experiences with signed numbers and absolute value in grade 6. You will use physical motion, number line models, and two-color counters to develop an understanding of the rules for operating with positive and negative numbers. You will then solve real-world and mathematical problems involving positive and negative rational numbers.

Topic 1 Adding and Subtracting Rational Numbers M2-3

Topic 2 Multiplying and Dividing Rational Numbers M2-85

TOPIC 1

Adding and Subtracting Rational Numbers

Death Valley has some very high and very low elevations: Badwater Basin is the point of the lowest elevation in North America, at 282 feet below sea level, while Telescope Peak in the Panamint Range has an elevation of 11,043 feet. Photo by Tuxyso / Wikimedia Commons, CC BY-SA 3.0, https://commons.wikimedia.org/w/index.php?curid=28603629

Lesson 1
Math Football
Using Models to Understand Integer Addition M2-7

Lesson 2
Walk the Line
Adding Integers, Part I. M2-17

Lesson 3
Two-Color Counters
Adding Integers, Part II M2-31

Lesson 4
What's the Difference?
Subtracting Integers. M2-49

Lesson 5
All Mixed Up
Adding and Subtracting Rational Numbers M2-69

Module 2: Operating with Signed Numbers

TOPIC 1: ADDING AND SUBTRACTING RATIONAL NUMBERS

In this topic, students use number lines and two-color counters to model addition and subtraction of integers before developing rules for determining the sum and difference of signed numbers. Students are expected to make connections among the representations used. After they understand what it means to add and subtract integers, students apply the rules to the set of rational numbers.

Where have we been?

In grade 6, students learned how to represent positive and negative rational numbers on a number line. They also know that $-p$ is p units from 0 on the number line and that $|p| = |-p| = p$. Students used number lines to model the distance from 0 and to model the distance between two rational numbers represented on vertical or horizontal number lines.

Where are we going?

Students will develop a strong conceptual foundation for adding and subtracting with rational numbers to provide the foundation for manipulating and representing increasingly complex numeric and algebraic expressions in later lessons and future courses and grades.

Using a Number Line to Model Adding and Subtracting Integers

A number line can be used to model adding and subtracting negative numbers. This number line models the sum $5 + (-8)$.

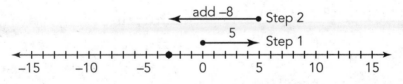

Myth: Students only use 10% of their brains.

Hollywood is in love with the idea that humans only use a small portion of their brains. This notion formed the basis of the movies *Lucy* (2014) and *Limitless* (2011). Both films ask the audience: Imagine what you could accomplish if you could use 100% of your brain!

Well, this isn't Hollywood, and you're stuck with an ordinary brain. The good news is that you **do** use 100% of your brain. As you look around the room, your visual cortex is busy assembling images; your motor cortex is busy moving your neck; and all of the associative areas recognize the objects that you see. Meanwhile, the corpus callosum, which is a thick band of neurons that connect the two hemispheres, ensures that all of this information is kept coordinated. Moreover, the brain does this automatically, which frees up space to ponder deep, abstract concepts...like mathematics!

#mathmythbusted

Talking Points

You can further support your student's learning by asking questions about the work they do in class or at home. Your student is learning to reason using signed numbers.

Questions to Ask

- How does this problem look like something you did in class?
- Can you show me the strategy you used to solve this problem? Do you know another way to solve it?
- Does your answer make sense? How do you know?
- Is there anything you don't understand? How can you use today's lesson to help?

Key Terms

absolute value
The absolute value of a number is its distance from 0 on a number line.

additive inverse
The additive inverse of a number is the opposite of the number: $-x$ is the additive inverse of x. Two numbers with the sum of zero are called additive inverses.

zero pair
A zero pair is a pair of numbers whose sum is zero. The value of negative 1 plus positive 1 is zero. So, negative 1 and positive 1 together are a zero pair.

Math Football

Using Models to Understand Integer Addition

1

WARM UP

Sketch a number line and plot each value.

1. -3
2. 0
3. 1
4. $\frac{1}{2}$
5. 3

LEARNING GOALS

- Represent numbers as positive and negative integers.
- Use a number line diagram to represent the sum of positive and negative integers.

You have learned about negative numbers and can plot locations on a number line. Does addition and subtraction work the same with negative numbers as with positive numbers?

Hut! Hut! Hike!

The playing field and footballs are located at the end of the lesson. You also need two number cubes, one red and one black.

You and a partner are going to play **Math Football**. You will take turns rolling two number cubes to determine how many yards you can advance the football toward your end zone.

Player 1 will be the Home Team and Player 2 will be the Visiting Team. In the first half, the Home Team will move toward the Home end zone, and the Visiting Team will move toward the Visiting end zone.

Rules

Players both start at the zero yard line and take turns. On your turn, roll two number cubes, one red and one black. The number on each cube represents a number of yards. Move your football to the left the number of yards shown on the red cube. Move your football to the right the number of yards shown on the black cube. Start each of your next turns from the ending position of your previous turn.

Scoring

When players reach their end zone, they score 6 points. If players reach their opponent's end zone, they lose 2 points. An end zone begins on either the +10 or −10 yard line.

Example:

	Player	Starting Position	Results of the Number Cubes Roll	Ending Position
First Turn	Home Team	0	Red 3 and Black 5	+2
	Visiting Team	0	Red 5 and Black 6	+1
Second Turn	Home Team	+2	Red 1 and Black 6	+7
	Visiting Team	+1	Red 6 and Black 2	−3

1. **Read through the table. After two turns, which player is closest to their end zone?**

ACTIVITY 1.1 Signed Numbers as Values with Directions

Let's play Math Football. Begin by selecting the home or visiting team. Your teacher will set the length of time for each half. You will play two halves. Make sure to switch ends at half-time with the Home Team moving toward the Visiting end zone, and the Visiting Team moving toward the Home end zone. Good luck!

1. Once your game is finished, answer each question.

   a. When you are trying to get to the Home end zone, which number cube do you want to show the greater value? Explain your reasoning.

   b. When you are trying to get to the Visiting end zone, which number cube do you want to show the greater value? Explain your reasoning.

   c. Did you ever find yourself back at the same position you ended on your previous turn? Describe the values on the cubes that would cause this to happen.

   d. Describe the roll that causes you to move your football the greatest distance either left or right.

ACTIVITY 1.2
Writing Equations with Signed Numbers

You can write equations to describe the results of number cube rolls. Think of the result of rolling the red number cube as a negative number and the result of rolling the black number cube as a positive number.

	Player	Starting Position	Results of the Number Cubes Roll	Ending Position	Number Sentence
First Turn	Home Team	0	Red 3 and Black 5	+2	$0 + (-3) + 5 = +2$
First Turn	Visiting Team	0	Red 5 and Black 6	+1	$0 + (-5) + 6 = +1$
Second Turn	Home Team	+2	Red 1 and Black 6	+7	$+2 + (-1) + 6 = +7$
Second Turn	Visiting Team	+1	Red 6 and Black 2	-3	$+1 + (-6) + 2 = -3$

1. **Describe each part of the number sentence for the second turn of the Visiting Team player.**

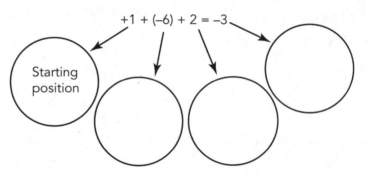

Starting position

$+1 + (-6) + 2 = -3$

Play Math Football again. But this time, work with your partner to get to the Home end zone together in the first half and the Visiting end zone in the second half. Write equations to record your moves.

2. **Think about the number cube rolls you made in the game.**

   a. **What kind of rolls move you closer to the Home end zone?**

   b. **What kind of rolls move you closer to the Visiting end zone?**

3. Write an equation for each situation. Use the game board for help.

I calculated the result from the two cubes first and then added this to the starting number. Can I do that?

a. The Home Team player starts at the zero yard line and rolls a red 6 and a black 2. What is the ending position?

Equation: _____

b. The Visiting Team player starts at the zero yard line and rolls a red 5 and a black 4. What is the ending position?

Equation: _____

c. The Home Team player starts at the 5 yard line and rolls a red 2 and a black 2. What is the ending position?

Equation: _____

d. The Visiting Team player starts at the −5 yard line and rolls a red 4 and a black 6. What is the ending position?

Equation: _____

e. Suppose the Home Team player is at the +8 yard line. Complete the table and write two equations that will put the player into the Home end zone.

Starting Position	Roll of the Red Number Cube	Roll of the Black Number Cube	Equation
+8			
+8			

f. Suppose the Visiting Team player is at the −8 yard line. Complete the table and write two equations that will put the player into the Visiting end zone.

Starting Position	Roll of the Red Number Cube	Roll of the Black Number Cube	Equation
−8			
−8			

TALK the TALK

Mission: Possible, and Impossible

Consider the moves you made in the Math Football game.

1. In which direction would you move if you roll:

   a. a larger number on the black cube than on the red cube?

   b. a larger number on the red cube than on the black cube?

   c. two black cubes?

   d. a black cube and a red cube?

   e. two red cubes?

2. Is it possible to decrease in value if rolling two black cubes? Explain your reasoning.

3. Is it possible to increase in value if rolling two red cubes? Explain your reasoning.

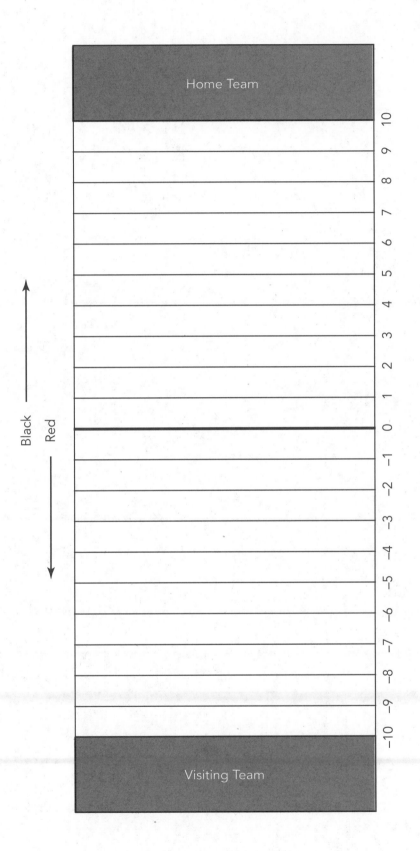

Home Team

10

9

8

7

6

5

4

3

2

1

Black

Red

0

−1

−2

−3

−4

−5

−6

−7

−8

−9

−10

Visiting Team

Assignment

Write

In your own words, explain how to decide whether the sum of two numbers is less than, equal to, or greater than 0.

Remember

Combining positive and negative moves together on a line results in a move to the left, a move to the right, or staying in the same position, depending on the size of the positive and negative values.

Practice

1. Determine the ending position by adding and subtracting the indicated steps from each starting position.

Starting Position	Steps Backward	Steps Forward	Ending Position
+3	4	5	
+7	6	2	
+5	2	4	
0	5	8	
−4	3	7	
+1	7	9	
−6	1	5	
−2	5	6	
8	3	1	
−9	2	4	

2. Write an equation to represent the movement indicated by the starting point, steps backward, and steps forward.

Starting Position	Steps Backward	Steps Forward	Equation
+2	4	7	
−7	3	5	
+6	9	4	
+4	6	1	
−5	2	9	
0	5	3	
−3	1	4	
−8	2	6	
0	8	2	
+9	7	8	

Stretch

Draw a model to represent the addition problem $-3\frac{1}{2} + (-1\frac{1}{4})$. Then determine the solution.

Review

1. Solve each proportion.

   a. $\dfrac{6.6}{p} = \dfrac{9}{12.15}$

   b. $\dfrac{8}{10.5} = \dfrac{c}{6.5625}$

2. Describe which method (scaling, unit rate, or means and extremes) you would use to solve for each variable and explain why.

   a. $\dfrac{2}{3} = \dfrac{20}{x}$

   b. $\dfrac{16}{4} = \dfrac{100}{x}$

3. Determine if each rectangle is a scale drawing of the given rectangle. Explain why or why not.

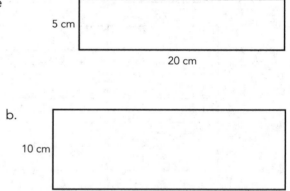

5 cm

20 cm

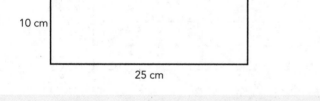

a.

10 cm

25 cm

b.

10 cm

40 cm

Walk the Line

2

Adding Integers, Part I

WARM UP

A large hotel has a ground floor (street level) and 26 floors of guest rooms above street level, which can be modeled by positive integers. There are 5 floors of parking below street level, which can be modeled by negative integers. In this hotel, street level is represented by zero.

Write an integer addition problem that models the hotel elevator's motion in each case.

1. The elevator starts at street level, goes up 7 floors, and then goes down 3 floors.

2. The elevator starts at street level, goes up 10 floors, and then goes down 12 floors.

3. The elevator starts at street level, goes down 4 floors, and then goes up 11 floors.

4. The elevator starts at street level, goes down 2 floors, goes up 5 floors, and finally goes down 3 floors.

LEARNING GOALS
- Model the addition of integers on a number line.
- Develop a rule for adding integers.
- Identify $p + q$ as the number located a distance of $|q|$ from p.

KEY TERM
- absolute value

You have been adding and subtracting positive numbers most of your life. In elementary school, you learned how to add numbers using a number line. How can a number line be a helpful tool in adding positive and negative numbers?

Getting on Line

Use the number line and determine the number described by each. Explain your reasoning.

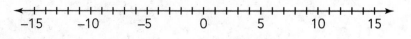

1. the number that is 7 more than −9

2. the number that is 2 more than −6

3. the number that is 10 more than −8

4. the number that is 10 less than 6

5. the number that is 5 less than −4

6. the number that is 2 less than −4

Walking the Number Line

Walking a number line can help you to add positive and negative numbers.

Walk the number line for an addition sentence:

- Start at zero and walk to the value of the first term of the expression.
- To indicate addition, turn to face up the number line, towards the greater positive numbers.
- Walk forward if adding a positive number or walk backward if adding a negative number.

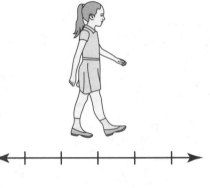

Your teacher will select a classmate to walk the line for each of the given problems. Help your classmate by preparing the directions that are needed.

1. **Complete the table.**

	Where You Start	Direction You Face	Walk Backwards or Forwards	Final Location
1 + 3				
0 + (−4)				
−3 + 5				
−1 + (−4)				

This worked example represents the movement created by walking the number line.

WORKED EXAMPLE

A number line can be used to model integer addition.
When adding a positive integer, move to the right on a number line.
When adding a negative integer, move to the left on a number line.

Example 1: The number line shows how to determine $5 + 8$.

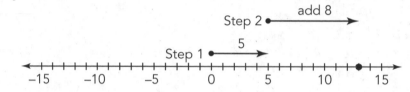

Example 2: The number line shows how to determine $5 + (-8)$.

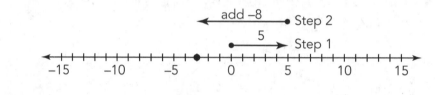

Compare the first steps in each example.

2. **What distance is shown by the first term in each example?**

Remember that the **absolute value** of a number is its distance from 0.

3. **Describe the graphical representation of the first term. Where does it start and in which direction does it move? How does this movement represent walking the line?**

4. **What is the absolute value of the first term in each example?**

Compare the second steps in each example.

5. What distance is shown by the second term in each example?

6. Why did the arrows for the second terms both start at the endpoints of the first terms but then continue in opposite directions? Explain your reasoning.

7. What is the absolute value of the second term in each example?

8. Use the number line to determine each sum. Show your work.

_____

Think about walking the line as you model these sums on the number line.

_____

a. −3 + 7 = _____

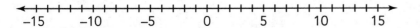

-15   -10   -5   0   5   10   15

b. 3 + (−7) = _____

-15   -10   -5   0   5   10   15

c. −3 + (−7) = _____

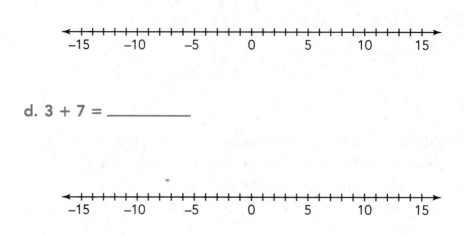

d. 3 + 7 = _____

Notice that the first term in each expression in parts (a) through (d) was either 3 or (−3).

9. **What do you notice about the distances shown by these terms on the number lines?**

10. **What is the absolute value of each term?**

Notice that the second term in each expression was either 7 or (−7).

11. **What do you notice about the distances shown by these terms on the number lines?**

12. **What is the absolute value of each term?**

ACTIVITY 2.2

Adding on Number Lines

Now that you have the feel for how to move on the number line when adding negative numbers, it is time to practice with more examples.

Use the number line to determine each sum. Show your work.

1. −9 + 5 = _____

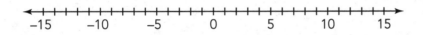

2. 9 + (−5) = _____

3. −9 + (−5) = _____

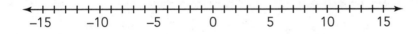

4. 9 + 5 = _____

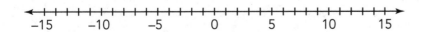

Notice that the first term in each expression in Questions 1 through 4 was either 9 or (−9).

5. **What do you notice about the distances shown by these terms on the number lines?**

6. **What is the absolute value of each term?**

How is knowing the absolute value of each term important?

Notice that the second term in each expression was either 5 or (−5).

7. **What do you notice about the distances shown by these terms on the number lines?**

8. **What is the absolute value of each term?**

Use the number line to determine each sum. Show your work.

9. −8 + 2 = _____

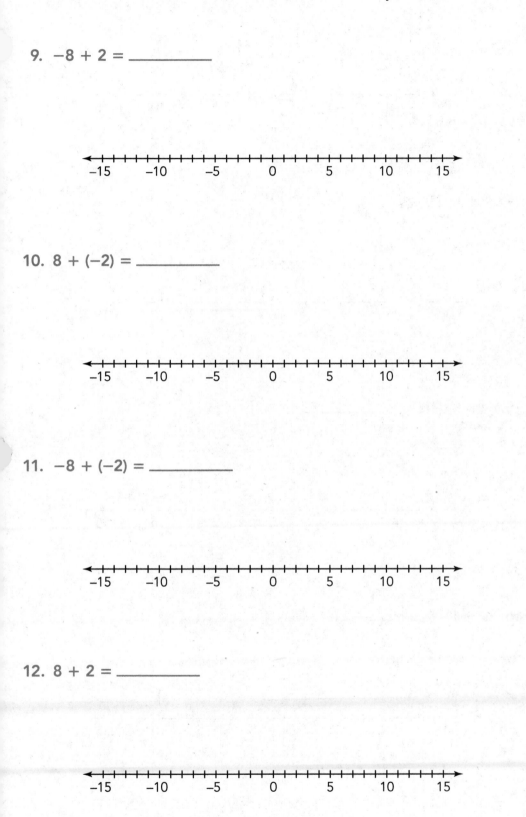

10. 8 + (−2) = _____

11. −8 + (−2) = _____

12. 8 + 2 = _____

13. −4 + 11 = _____

14. 4 + (−11) = _____

15. −4 + (−11) = _____

Can you see why the absolute value is important when adding and subtracting signed numbers?

16. 4 + 11 = _____

TALK the TALK

Patterns on the Line

Demonstrate what you have learned about adding two numbers using a number line.

1. Describe the patterns from the *Adding on Number Lines* activity, when you:

   a. add two positive numbers.

   b. add two negative numbers.

   c. add a negative and a positive number.

2. Do you think these patterns will hold true for all numbers, even fractions and decimals? Explain your reasoning.

3. Complete each number line model and number sentence.

a. 4 + _____ = 12

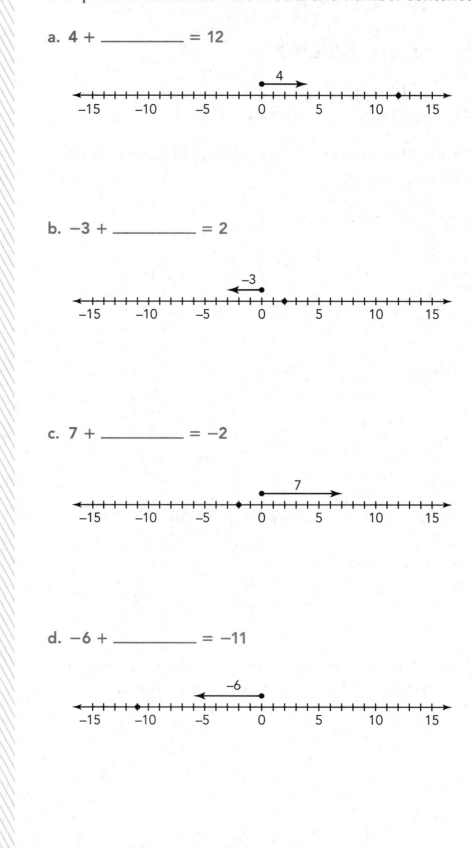

b. −3 + _____ = 2

c. 7 + _____ = −2

d. −6 + _____ = −11

Assignment

Write

Explain how walking the line is the same as representing addition and subtraction on the number line.

Remember

When adding a positive integer on a number line, move to the right on the number line. When adding a negative integer, move to the left on the number line.

Practice

Use the number line to determine each sum. Show your work.

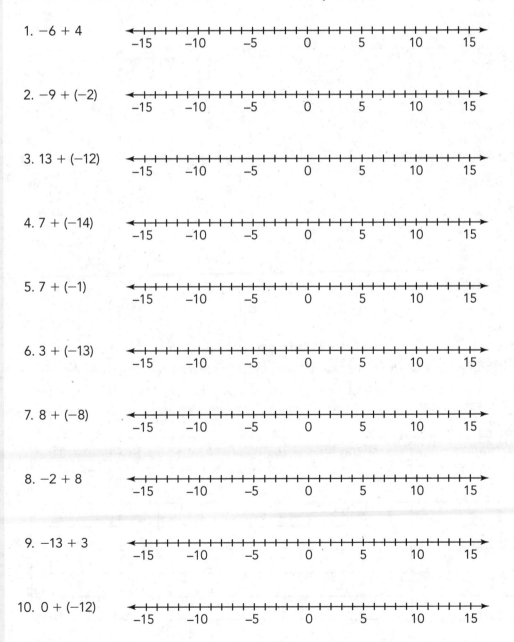

1. $-6 + 4$

2. $-9 + (-2)$

3. $13 + (-12)$

4. $7 + (-14)$

5. $7 + (-1)$

6. $3 + (-13)$

7. $8 + (-8)$

8. $-2 + 8$

9. $-13 + 3$

10. $0 + (-12)$

Complete each number line model and number sentence.

1. $-4 +$ _____ $= 0$

2. $-15 +$ _____ $= -9$

3. _____ $+ 10 = -2$

4. _____ $+ (-11) = -4$

5. $-12 +$ _____ $= -14$

Stretch

Draw a number line model to determine each sum.

1. $-1.6 + -0.7$

2. $-2.1 + 0.8$

3. $2.2 + -4.1$

Review

Northern Tier Gardens has hired you for a summer job installing water gardens. They have circular water garden pools available in a variety of sizes. The manager has asked you to create a table to show the circumference and area of the company's various water garden pools. Use 3.14 for π and round each answer to the nearest hundredth.

Garden Name	Radius (feet)	Diameter (feet)	Area (square feet)	Circumference (feet)
Atlantic	2.5	5		
Pacifica	6	12		
Mediterranean	1.75	3.5		
Baltica	1	2		
Japanesque	2.25	4.5		
Floridian	3.25	6.5		

Two-Color Counters

Adding Integers, Part II

WARM UP

Use a number line to determine each sum.
Then write a sentence to describe the movement you used on the number line to compute the sum of the two integers.

1. $-2 + 1$

2. $-5 + 8$

3. $-2 + (-3)$

4. $4 + (-6)$

LEARNING GOALS

- Describe situations in which opposite quantities combine to make 0.
- Model the addition of integers using two-color counters.
- Develop a rule for adding integers.
- Apply previous understandings of addition and subtraction to add rational numbers.

KEY TERM

- additive inverses

You know how to use a number line to model adding positive and negative numbers. Do the patterns you noticed from the number line model apply to other models for adding positive and negative numbers?

Creating Zero

Use a number line to illustrate how the sum of two numbers can be zero.

> How can you end at zero if you start at zero?

1. Write 3 examples of number sentences that sum to zero and draw the number line models to support your solutions.

2. What pattern do you notice?

3. Describe a real-life situation in which two numbers would sum to zero. Write the number sentence that could be used to represent the situation.

Additive Inverses

Addition of integers can also be modeled using two-color counters that represent positive (+) charges and negative (−) charges. One color, usually red, represents the negative number, or negative charge. The other color, usually yellow, represents the positive number, or positive charge. In this book, gray shading will represent the negative number, and no shading will represent the positive number.

$$\ominus = -1 \qquad \oplus = +1$$

Two numbers with the sum of zero are called **additive inverses**.

WORKED EXAMPLE

You can model the expression 3 + (−3) in different ways using two-color counters:

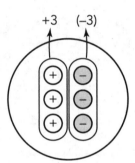

Three positive charges and three negative charges have no charge.

3 + (−3) = 0

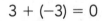

Each positive charge is paired with a negative charge.

Each pair of positive and negative charges has no charge.

3 + (−3) = 0

> Can you create two-color counter models of the sums you wrote in the *Creating Zero* activity?

1. What is the value of each ⊕ and ⊖ pair in the second model?

2. Describe how you can change the numbers of ⊕ and ⊖ counters in the model but leave the sum unchanged.

ACTIVITY 3.2

Adding Integers with Two-Color Counters

Let's consider two examples where integers are added using two-color counters.

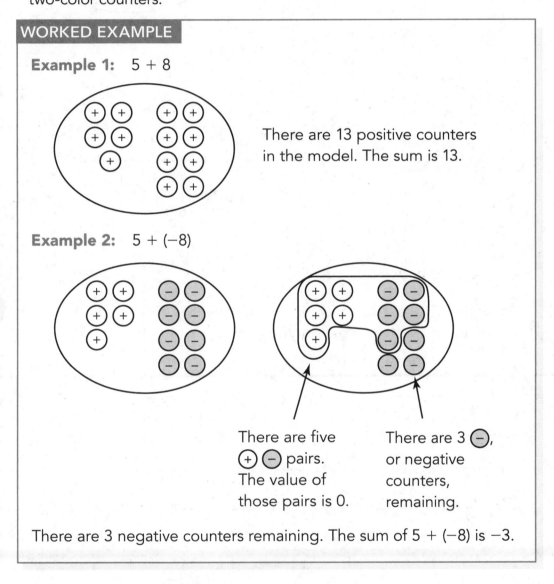

WORKED EXAMPLE

Example 1: $5 + 8$

There are 13 positive counters in the model. The sum is 13.

Example 2: $5 + (-8)$

There are five ⊕ ⊖ pairs. The value of those pairs is 0.

There are 3 ⊖, or negative counters, remaining.

There are 3 negative counters remaining. The sum of $5 + (-8)$ is -3.

1. Create another model to represent a sum of -3. Write the appropriate number sentence.

2. Share your model with your classmates. How are they the same? How are they different?

In an addition sentence, the terms being added together are called addends.

3. Write a number sentence to represent each model.

a.

b.

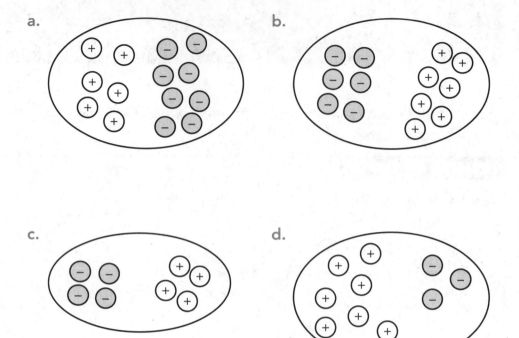

c.

d.

4. Does the order in which you wrote the integers in your number sentence matter? How do you know?

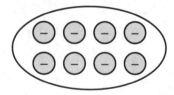

The students were then asked to write a number sentence for the given model.

Ava 👍

$-8 + 0 = -8$

Landon 👍

$-1 + (-7) = -8$

5. Analyze the number sentences written by Ava and Landon.

   a. Explain why both number sentences are correct.

   b. Write an additional number sentence that could describe the model.

6. Write each number sentence in Question 5 a second way.

Ava and Landon used two-color counters to represent the number sentence 3 + (−5).

7. The students placed the same counters on their desks, but they reported different sums. Ava reported the sum as 8 and Landon said the sum was −2. Use the model to explain who is correct. What was the error made by the incorrect student?

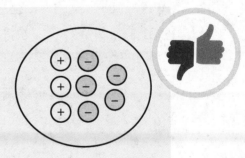

8. **Draw a model for each, and then complete the number sentence.**

   a. $-9 + (-4) =$ _____

   b. $-9 + 4 =$ _____

   c. $9 + (-4) =$ _____

   d. $9 + 4 =$ _____

9. **Complete the model to determine the unknown integer.**

   a. $1 +$ _____ $= -4$

   b. $-3 +$ _____ $= 7$

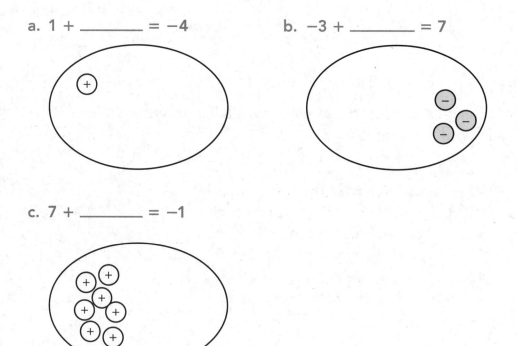

   c. $7 +$ _____ $= -1$

10. Describe the set of integers that makes each sentence true.

   a. What integer(s) when added to −7 give a sum greater than 0?

   b. What integer(s) when added to −7 give a sum less than 0?

   c. What integer(s) when added to −7 give a sum of 0?

You have now used two models to represent adding integers.

11. For each problem, draw both models to represent the number sentences and determine the sums.

   a. (−6) + 13

   b. 8 + (−13)

   c. (−3) + (−7)

   d. 2 + 9

   Think about how the absolute values of the addends compare with each other.
   ---

12. Explain the similarities and differences of the models in helping you determine the sum of two integers.

Rules for Adding Integers

Visual models provide concrete representations of new ideas, like adding signed numbers. But you probably do not want to draw visual models when you have large numbers, lots of addends, fractions, or decimals.

Look back over the activities in this lesson and write rules for adding integers.

What happens when you add a negative and a positive integer and they both have the same absolute value?

1. **When adding two integers, what will the sign of the sum be if:**

    a. **both integers are positive?**

    b. **both integers are negative?**

    c. **one integer is positive and one integer is negative?**

2. **Write a rule that states how to determine the sum of any two integers that have the same sign.**

3. **Write a rule that states how to determine the sum of any two integers that have opposite signs.**

Cut out the sums provided at the end of the lesson.

4. Without computing the sums, sort the number sentences into two piles: those that have a positive sum and those that have a negative sum.

    a. How can you decide which number sentences have a positive sum and which have a negative sum?

    b. Tape or glue the number sentences in the space provided.

    Positive Sums   **Negative Sums**

    c. Use your rules to determine the sum of each number sentence.

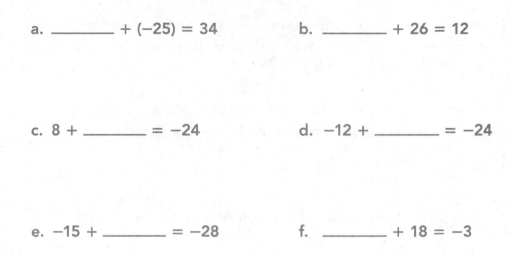

5. Determine each unknown addend.

a. _____ + (−25) = 34

b. _____ + 26 = 12

c. 8 + _____ = −24

d. −12 + _____ = −24

e. −15 + _____ = −28

f. _____ + 18 = −3

TALK the TALK

Summarizing Sums

1. Use the graphic organizer provided to represent additive inverses. Write an example, using both a number sentence and a real-life situation. Then represent your number sentence in words, using a number line model, and using a two-color counter model.

EXAMPLE: NUMBER
SENTENCE AND
REAL-LIFE SITUATION

IN WORDS

ADDITIVE INVERSES
AND ZERO

NUMBER LINE MODEL

TWO-COLOR COUNTER
MODEL

2. Write a number sentence that meets the given conditions. If it is not possible to create the number sentence, explain why not.

   a. Two positive addends with a positive sum.

   b. Two positive addends with a negative sum.

   c. Two negative addends with a positive sum.

   d. Two negative addends with a negative sum.

   e. A positive addend and a negative addend with a positive sum.

   f. A positive addend and a negative addend with a negative sum.

Rules for Adding Integers Cutouts

−58 + 24	−35 + (−15)
−33 + (−12)	−48 + 60
26 + (−13)	67 + 119
−105 + 25	153 + (−37)
21 + (−56)	18 + (−17)

Assignment

Write

Define the term *additive inverse* in your own words.

Remember

When two integers have the same sign and are added together, the sign of the sum is the sign of both integers.

When two integers have opposite signs and are added together, the absolute values of the integers are subtracted and the sign of the sum is the sign of the integer with the greater absolute value.

Practice

1. Write a number sentence for each two-color counter model. Then determine the sum.

   a. 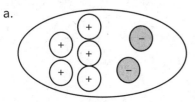   b.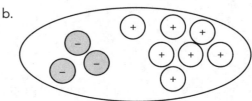

2. Draw a two-color counter model for each number sentence. Then determine the sum.

   a. 3 + (−6)   b. −7 + (−4)

   c. 2 + 5   d. 10 + (−8)

3. An atom is made up of protons, neutrons, and electrons. The protons carry a positive ⊕ charge and make up the nucleus of an atom with the neutrons. Neutrons do not carry a charge. The electrons carry a negative ⊖ charge and circle the nucleus. Atoms have no positive or negative charge. This means that they must have the same number of protons and electrons. A partial model of a nitrogen atom is shown.

   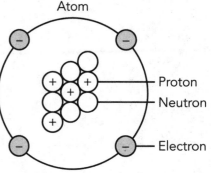

   a. How many electrons should be drawn on the model of a nitrogen atom so that it has the same number of protons and electrons? How did you know?

   b. Complete the model of the nitrogen atom by drawing in the electrons.

   c. Write a number sentence to represent the sum of the number of protons and electrons in a nitrogen atom.

   d. Use a number line to show the sum of the number of protons and electrons in the nitrogen atom.

   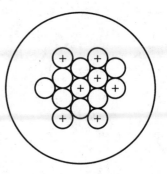

Determine each sum.

4. 45 + (−27)   5. 32 + (−98)

6. −153 + 74   7. −63 + (−41)

8. 527 + (−289)   9. −32 + 98

10. −47 + (−95)   11. −51 + 134

Stretch

Determine each sum.

1. $21\frac{3}{8} + \left(-51\frac{1}{4}\right)$

2. $-65\frac{2}{5} + 103$

3. $-34.528 + 78.12$

4. $863.78 + (-1024.01)$

Review

Use a number line to determine each sum.

1. $-3 + 4$

2. $-3 + (-4)$

Calculate the sale price of each item.

3. A pair of headphones is on sale for 15% off the original price of $305.

4. A hoverboard is on sale for 10% off the original price of $247.50.

Solve each proportion.

5. $\frac{3}{4} = \frac{x}{18}$

6. $\frac{5}{8} = \frac{21}{x}$

What's the Difference?

4

Subtracting Integers

WARM UP

For each number line model, write the number sentence described by the model and draw a two-color counter model to represent the number sentence.

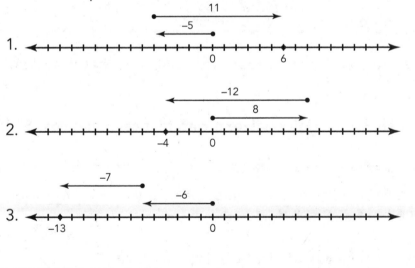

1.

2.

3.

LEARNING GOALS

- Model subtraction of integers on a number line.
- Model subtraction of integers using two-color counters.
- Develop a rule for subtracting integers.
- Apply previous understandings of addition and subtraction to subtract rational numbers.

KEY TERM

- zero pair

You have added integers using number lines and two-color counter models. How can you use these models to subtract integers?

Take It Away

Each situation described has two different conclusions. Describe how you might model each on a number line.

1. **You owe your friend $10.**

    a. **You borrow an additional $5.**

    b. **Your friend takes away $5 of that debt.**

> Each situation can be modeled by a subtraction problem. Try to write it!

2. **The temperature is −7°.**

    a. **Overnight it gets 12° colder.**

    b. **During the day, it gets 12° warmer.**

3. **You have charged $65 on a credit card.**

    a. **You return an item purchased with that card that cost $24.**

    b. **You purchase an additional item with that card that cost $24.**

4. **You dug a hole in the ground that is 20 inches deep. Your dog sees the pile of dirt and thinks it's a game.**

    a. **He knocks 6 inches of dirt back into the hole.**

    b. **He digs the hole another 4 inches deeper.**

Subtracting Integers on a Number Line

Think about how you moved on the number line when you were learning to add positive and negative numbers in the previous lesson. Let's walk the line to generate rules for subtracting integers.

Walk the number line for a subtraction sentence:

- Start at zero and walk to the value of the first term of the expression.
- To indicate subtraction, turn to face down the number line, towards the lesser negative numbers.
- Walk forward if subtracting a positive number or walk backward if subtracting a negative number.

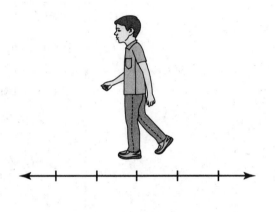

Your teacher will select a classmate to walk the line for each of the given problems. Help your classmate by preparing the directions that are needed.

1. **Complete the table.**

	Where You Start	Direction You Face on the Number Line	Walk Backwards or Forwards	Final Location
$1 - 3$				
$0 - (-4)$				
$-3 - 5$				
$-1 - (-4)$				

Cara thought about how she could take what she learned from walking the line and create a number line model on paper. She said, "Subtraction means to move in the opposite direction."

Analyze Cara's examples.

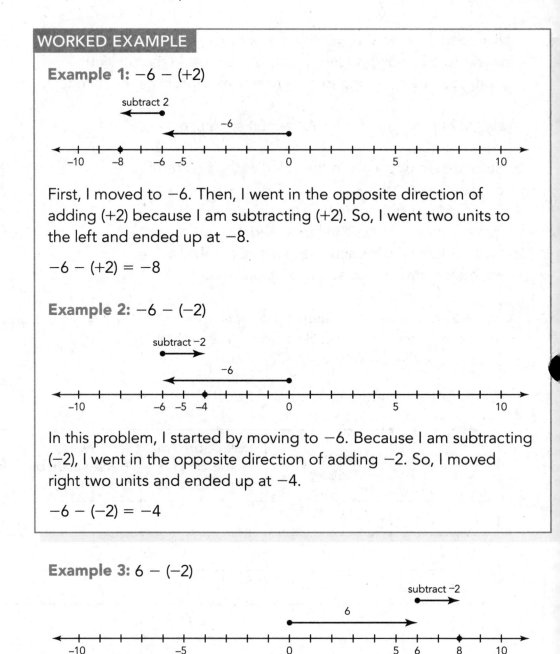

WORKED EXAMPLE

Example 1: −6 − (+2)

First, I moved to −6. Then, I went in the opposite direction of adding (+2) because I am subtracting (+2). So, I went two units to the left and ended up at −8.

−6 − (+2) = −8

Example 2: −6 − (−2)

In this problem, I started by moving to −6. Because I am subtracting (−2), I went in the opposite direction of adding −2. So, I moved right two units and ended up at −4.

−6 − (−2) = −4

Example 3: 6 − (−2)

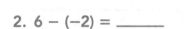

2. 6 − (−2) = _____

Explain the movement Cara modeled on the number line to determine the answer.

Example 4: 6 − (+2)

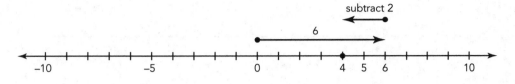

3. 6 − (+2) = _____

   Explain the movement Cara modeled on the number line to
   determine the answer.

4. Use the number line to complete each number sentence.

   a. −4 − (−3) = _____

   b. −4 − (−4) = _____

   c. −4 − 3 = _____

   d. −4 − 4 = _____

   e. 4 − (−3) = _____

> Use Cara's examples for help.

f. 4 − 4 = _____

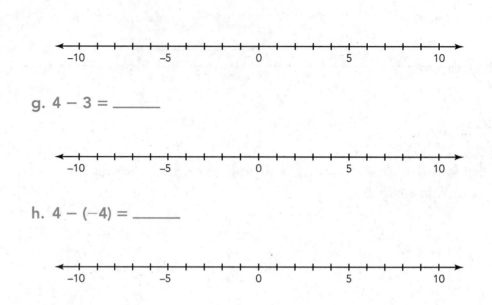

g. 4 − 3 = _____

h. 4 − (−4) = _____

5. What patterns did you notice when subtracting the integers in Question 4? Describe an addition problem that is similar to each subtraction problem.

a. Subtracting two negative integers

b. Subtracting two positive integers

c. Subtracting a positive integer from a negative integer

d. Subtracting a negative integer from a positive integer

Subtracting Integers with Two-Color Counters

The number line model and the two-color counter model used in the addition of integers can also be used to investigate the subtraction of integers.

Subtraction can mean to "take away" objects from a set. Subtraction can also mean a comparison of two numbers, or the "difference between them."

WORKED EXAMPLE

Using just positive or just negative counters, you can show subtraction using the "take away" model.

Example 1: 7 − 5
First, start with seven positive counters.

Then, take away five positive counters.   Two positive counters remain.

$$7 - 5 = 2$$

Example 2: −7 − (−5)
First, start with seven negative counters.

Then, take away five negative counters.   Two negative counters remain.

$$-7 - (-5) = -2$$

1. How are Examples 1 and 2 similar? How are these examples different?

To subtract integers using both positive and negative counters, you will need to use *zero pairs*.

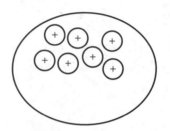

Recall that the value of a ⊖ and ⊕ pair is zero. So, together they form a **zero pair**. You can add as many pairs as you need and not change the value.

WORKED EXAMPLE

Example 3: 7 − (−5)

Start with seven positive counters.

The expression says to subtract five negative counters, but there are no negative counters in the first model. Insert five negative counters into the model. So that you don't change the value, you must also insert five positive counters.

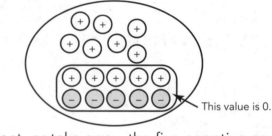

This value is 0.

Now, you can subtract, or take away, the five negative counters.

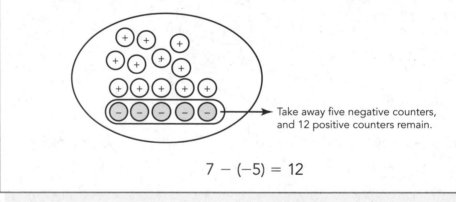

Take away five negative counters, and 12 positive counters remain.

$$7 - (-5) = 12$$

---

2. Why is the second model equivalent to the original model?

Example 4: −7 − 5

Start with seven negative counters.

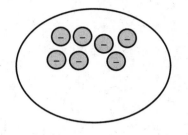

3. The expression says to subtract five positive counters, but there are no positive counters in the first model.

   a. How can you insert positive counters into the model and not change the value?

   b. Complete the model.

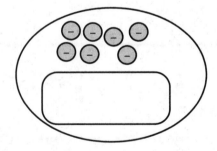

> This is a little bit like regrouping in subtraction.

   c. Now, subtract, or take away, the five positive counters. Determine the difference.

4. Draw a representation for each subtraction problem. Then, calculate the difference.

a. $4 - (-5)$

b. $-4 - (-5)$

c. $-4 - 5$

d. $4 - 5$

5. How could you model 0 − (−7)?

   a. Draw a sketch of your model. Then, determine
      the difference.

   b. In part (a), does it matter how many zero pairs you add?
      Explain your reasoning.

6. Does the order in which you subtract two numbers matter?
   Draw models and provide examples to explain your reasoning.

7. Are the rules you wrote at the end of the previous activity true
   for the two-color counter models? What else did you learn
   about subtracting integers?

You probably have noticed some patterns when subtracting signed numbers on the number line and with two-color counters. Let's explore these patterns to develop a rule.

$-8 - 5 = -13$

$-8 - 4 = -12$

$-8 - 3 = -11$

$-8 - 2 = -10$

$-8 - 1 = -9$

$-8 - 0 = -8$

1. Analyze the number sentences shown.

   a. What patterns do you see? What happens as the integer subtracted from -8 decreases?

   b. From your pattern, predict the answer to $-8 - (-1)$.

Consider the subtraction expression $-8 - (-2)$.

Cara's Method 👍
Start at -8. Since I'm subtracting, you go in the opposite direction of adding (-2), which means I go to the right 2 units. The answer is -6.

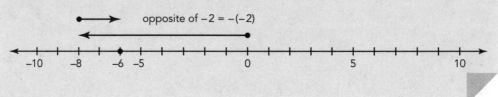

Neveah's Method 👍
I see another pattern. Since subtraction is the inverse of addition, you can think of subtraction as adding the opposite number.

$-8 - (-2)$ is the same as $-8 + (+2)$

$-8 + 2 = -6$

2. How is Neveah's method similar to Cara's method?

3. Use Neveah's method to fill in each blank.

   $10 - (-4) = 10 + ($ _____ $) = $ _____

4. Determine each difference.

   a. $-9 - (-2) = $ b. $-3 - (-3) = $

   c. $-7 - 5 = $ d. $24 - 8 = $

   e. $-4 - 2 = $ f. $5 - 9 = $

   g. $-20 - (-30) = $ h. $-10 - 18 = $

5. Determine the unknown integer in each number sentence.

   a. $3 + $ _____ $= 7$ b. $2 + $ _____ $= -7$

   c. _____ $+ -20 = -10$ d. _____ $- 5 = 40$

   e. _____ $- (-5) = 40$ f. _____ $+ 5 = 40$

   g. $6 + $ _____ $= 52$ h. $-6 + $ _____ $= 52$

   i. $-6 + $ _____ $= -52$

I can change any subtraction problem to addition if I add the opposite of the number that follows the subtraction sign.

Distance Between Rational Numbers

Amusement parks are constantly trying to increase the level of thrills on their rides. One way is to make the roller coasters drop faster and farther. A certain roller coaster begins by climbing a hill that is 277 feet above ground. Riders go from the top of that hill to the bottom, which is in a tunnel 14 feet under ground, in approximately 3 seconds!

Determine the vertical distance from the top of the roller coaster to the bottom of the tunnel.

1. **Plot the height and depth of the first hill of the roller coaster on the number line.**

(number line with values 300, 250, 200, 150, 100, 50, 0, −30)

Consider Christian's and Mya's methods for determining the vertical distance.

Christian

In sixth grade, I learned that you could add the absolute values of each number to calculate the distance.

$$|277| + |-14| = 277 + 14$$

$$= 291$$

The vertical distance is 291 feet.

Mya

I learned in elementary school that the difference between two numbers on a number line can be determined with subtraction. Because absolute value measures distance, I need the absolute value of the difference.

$$|277 - (-14)| = |277 + (+14)|$$
$$= |291|$$
$$= 291$$

The vertical distance is 291 feet.

2. Describe how Christian and Mya used absolute value differently to determine the vertical distance from the top of the roller coaster to the bottom of the tunnel.

3. Carson wonders if order matters. Instead of calculating the distance from the top to the bottom, he wants to calculate the vertical distance from the bottom to the top. Is Carson correct? Determine if Carson is correct using both Christian's strategy and Mya's strategy.

As demonstrated in Mya's strategy, the distance between two numbers on the number line is the absolute value of their difference. Use Mya's strategy to solve each problem.

4. The first recorded Olympic Games began in 776 BCE. Called the *Ancient Olympics*, games were held every four years until being abolished by Roman Emperor Theodosius I in 393 CE.

   a. Represent the start and end years of the Ancient Olympic Games as integers.

   b. Determine the length of time between the start and end of the Ancient Olympic Games.

   c. Determine the length of time between the start of the Ancient Olympics and the Modern Olympics, which began in 1896.

   d. If you research the ancient calendar, you will learn that there actually was no Year 0. The calendar went from −1 BCE to 1 CE. Adjust your answer from part (c) to account for this.

5. On February 10, 2011, the temperature in Nowata, OK, hit a low of −31°. Over the course of the next week, the temperature increased to a high of 79°. How many degrees different was the low from the high temperature?

TALK the TALK

Determining the Difference

Use what you have learned about adding and subtracting with integers to think about patterns in addition and subtraction.

1. Determine whether these subtraction sentences are always true, sometimes true, or never true. Give examples to explain your thinking.

   a. positive − positive = positive

   b. negative − positive = negative

   c. positive − negative = negative

   d. negative − negative = negative

2. If you subtract two negative integers, will the answer be greater than or less than the number you started with? Explain your thinking.

3. What happens when a positive number is subtracted from zero?

4. What happens when a negative number is subtracted from zero?

5. Just by looking at the problem, how do you know if the sum of two integers is positive, negative, or zero?

6. How are addition and subtraction of integers related?

7. Write a rule for subtracting positive and negative integers.

Assignment

Write

Define the term *zero pair* in your own words.

Remember

You can change any subtraction problem to an addition problem without changing the answer. Subtracting two integers is the same as adding the opposite of the subtrahend, the number you are subtracting.

Practice

1. Draw both a model using two-color counters and a model using a number line to represent each number sentence. Then, determine the difference.
   a. $-8 - (-5)$
   b. $-4 - 9$
   c. $2 - (-8)$
   d. $3 - 12$

2. Determine each difference without using a number line.
   a. $7 - (-13)$ b. $10 - (-1)$
   c. $-16 - 3$ d. $-9 - 7$
   e. $-1 - (-2)$ f. $-5 - (-5)$
   g. $19 - (-19)$ h. $-8 - (-8)$
   i. $40 - (-20)$ j. $-800 - (-300)$

3. The highest temperature ever recorded on Earth was 136° F at Al Aziziyah, Libya, in Africa. The lowest temperature ever recorded on Earth was −129° F at Vostok Station in Antarctica. Plot each temperature as an integer on a number line, and use absolute value to determine the difference between the two temperatures.

4. The highest point in the United States is Mount McKinley, Alaska, at about 6773 yards above sea level. The lowest point in the United States is the Badwater Basin in Death Valley, California, at about 87 yards below sea level. Plot each elevation as an integer on a number line, and use absolute value to determine the number of yards between in the lowest and highest points.

Stretch

1. Determine each difference without using a number line.

   a. $3.1 - (-3.3)$

   b. $-8.3 - 8.8$

   c. $42.5 - 45.6$

   d. $-28.4 - (-79.5)$

2. The deepest point in the ocean is the Marianas Trench in the Pacific Ocean at about 6.9 miles below sea level. The highest point in the world is Mount Everest in the Himalayan Mountains at about 5.5 miles. Plot each elevation as an rational number on a number line, and use absolute value to determine the number of miles between the deepest point in the ocean and the highest point in the world.

Review

1. The city of Nashville, Tennessee, constructed an exact replica of the Parthenon. In 1982, construction began on a sculpture of Athena Parthenos, which stands 41 feet 10 inches tall.

   a. The sculptor first made a 1 : 10 model from clay. This means that 1 inch on the model is equal to 10 inches on the real statue. What was the height of the clay model?

   b. Later the sculptor made a 1 : 5 model. This means that 1 inch on the model is equal to 5 inches on the real statue. What was the height of the model?

2. Write and solve a proportion to answer each problem. Show all your work.

   a. Tommy types 50 words per minute, with an average of 3 mistakes. How many mistakes would you expect Tommy to make if he typed 300 words? Write your answer using a complete sentence.

   b. Six cans of fruit juice cost $2.50. Ned needs to buy 72 cans for a camping trip for the Outdoor Club. How much will he spend?

3. Solve each equation for x.

   a. $72 = 55 + x$

   b. $\frac{4}{5}x = 60$

All Mixed Up 5

Adding and Subtracting Rational Numbers

WARM UP

Determine each sum.

1. $\frac{1}{6} + \frac{1}{3}$

2. $\frac{2}{7} + \frac{2}{5}$

3. $\frac{1}{2} + \frac{3}{5}$

4. $\frac{1}{3} + \frac{4}{5}$

LEARNING GOALS

- Interpret and determine sums and differences of rational numbers in real-world contexts.
- Represent and apply the additive inverse in real-world contexts.
- Determine distance as the absolute value of the difference between two signed numbers in real-world contexts.
- Solve real-world and mathematical problems involving operations with rational numbers.

You have learned how to add and subtract with signed numbers using models and rules. How can you solve real-world problems by adding and subtracting signed numbers?

No Matter the Number

Consider this addition problem: $-3\frac{3}{4} + 4\frac{1}{4} = ?$

1. Draw a model to add the two numbers and determine the sum. Explain how your model represents the addition problem.

Remember, addends are the numbers being added.

2. How would your model be different if the addends were integers? How would the model be the same?

3. Describe how you can apply the rules you have learned about adding signed numbers to determine the sum of $-3\frac{3}{4}$ and $4\frac{1}{4}$.

Sum of Rational Numbers Problems

You can use what you know about adding and subtracting positive and negative integers to solve problems with positive and negative fractions and decimals.

Yesterday, Katrina was just $23.75 below her fundraising goal. She got a check today for $12.33 to put toward the fundraiser. Describe Katrina's progress toward the goal.

WORKED EXAMPLE

You can model this situation using addition:

$$-\$23.75 \quad + \quad \$12.33$$

currently below   got a check for
the goal   this amount

• Estimate.

Katrina will still be below her goal, because $-23.75 + 12.33 < 0$.

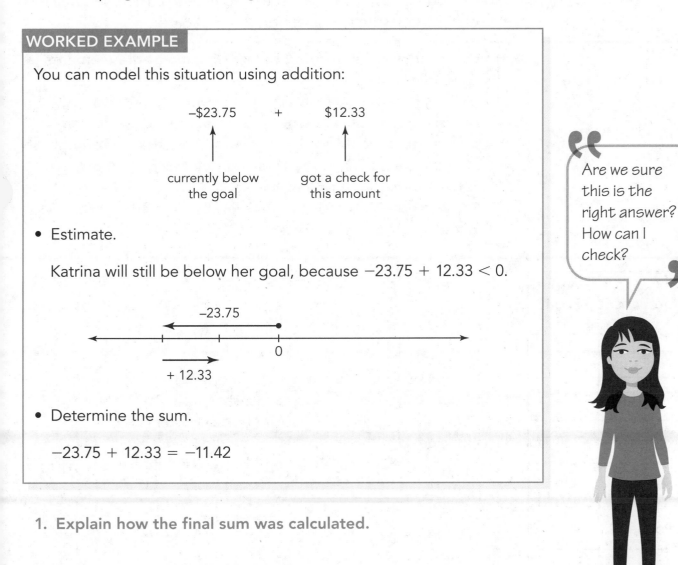

−23.75

+ 12.33

• Determine the sum.

$-23.75 + 12.33 = -11.42$

Are we sure this is the right answer? How can I check?

1. Explain how the final sum was calculated.

2. What does the sum mean in terms of the problem situation?

3. Explain how you can know that addition is the correct operation to use to solve this problem.

Sketch a model to estimate each sum or difference. Then determine each solution and write an equation.

4. The table shows the freezing points of some of the elements in the periodic table.

a. Patricia and Elliott are trying to figure out how much the temperature would have to increase from the freezing point of hydrogen to reach the freezing point of phosphorus. Patricia says the temperature would have to increase 545.7°, and Elliott says the temperature would have to increase 322.3°. Who is correct?

b. Francine and Lisa are trying to figure out how much the temperature would have to increase from the freezing point of nitrogen to reach the freezing point of mercury. Francine says the temperature would have to increase $308\frac{1}{20}°$, and Lisa says the temperature would have to increase $383\frac{9}{20}°$. Who is correct?

Element	Freezing Point (°F)
Helium	−458
Hydrogen	−434
Oxygen	−368.77
Nitrogen	$-345\frac{3}{4}$
Chlorine	−149.51
Mercury	$-37\frac{7}{10}$
Phosphorus	111.7

5. A drilling crew dug to a height of $-45\frac{1}{4}$ feet during their first day of drilling. On the second day, the crew dug down $9\frac{1}{3}$ feet more than on the first day. Describe the height of the bottom of the hole after the second day.

6. The ancient Babylonians were writing fractions in 1800 BCE. But they did not have a concept of zero until about 1489 years later. In what year did the Babylonians develop the concept of zero?

The abbreviation BCE means "before the common era," or before Year 0.

7. Ben purchased lunch today at the school cafeteria for $2.75. Before today, Ben owed $9.15 on his lunch account. What is the status of his lunch account after today?

8. The highest mountain in the world is Mt. Everest, whose peak is 29,029 feet above sea level. But the tallest mountain is Mauna Kea. The base of Mauna Kea is 19,669 feet below sea level, and its peak is 33,465 feet above its base. How much higher above sea level is Mt. Everest than Mauna Kea?

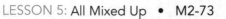

Rational Number Difference Problems

The freezing point of chlorine is –149.51° Fahrenheit. The element zinc freezes at much higher temperatures. The freezing point of zinc is 787.51° Fahrenheit. How many more degrees is the freezing point of zinc than the freezing point of chlorine?

WORKED EXAMPLE

You can model this situation using subtraction:

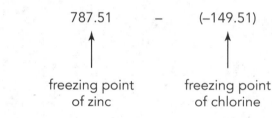

787.51   –   (–149.51)

freezing point of zinc   freezing point of chlorine

- Estimate.

  The answer is greater than 787.51, because $787.51-(-149.51) = 787.51 + 149.51$.

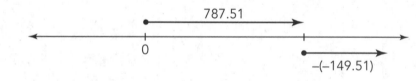

787.51

–(–149.51)

- Determine the difference. Write an equation.

  $787.51-(-149.51) = 937.02$

---

1. **What does the difference mean in terms of the problem situation?**

2. **Explain how you can check the answer.**

Sketch a model to estimate. Then determine each solution and write an equation.

3. The temperature in Wichita, Kansas, is −3°C. The temperature in Ryan's hometown is 18° colder than that. What is the temperature in Ryan's hometown?

4. To qualify to compete in the high jump finals, athletes must jump a certain height in the semi-finals. Clarissa jumped $2\frac{3}{8}$ inches below the qualifying height, but her friend Anika made it to $1\frac{5}{6}$ inches over the qualifying height. How much higher was Anika's semi-final jump compared with Clarissa's?

5. The Down Under roller coaster rises up to 65.8 feet above the ground before dropping 90 feet into an underground cavern. Describe the height of the roller coaster at the bottom of the cavern.

ACTIVITY 5.3

Adding and Subtracting Rational Numbers

Determine each sum or difference.

1. $4.7 + (-3.65)$

2. $-\frac{2}{3} + \frac{5}{8}$

3. $3.95 + (-6.792)$

4. $2\frac{5}{7} + \left(-1\frac{1}{3}\right)$

5. $-\frac{3}{4} + \frac{5}{8}$

6. $-7.38 - (-6.2)$

7. $-\frac{3}{4} - \frac{5}{8}$

8. $-2\frac{5}{6} + 1\frac{3}{8}$

9. $-\frac{7}{12} - \frac{5}{6}$

10. $-37.27 + (-13.2)$

11. $-0.8 - (-0.6)$

12. $2\frac{3}{7} + \left(-1\frac{3}{4}\right)$

13. $0.67 + (-0.33)$

14. $-42.65 - (-16.3)$

15. $-7300 + 2100$

16. $-3\frac{5}{8} - \left(-2\frac{1}{3}\right)$

17. $-4.7 + 3.16$

18. $26.9 - (-3.1)$

19. $-325 + (-775)$

20. $-2\frac{1}{5} - 1\frac{3}{10}$

TALK the TALK

Mixing Up the Sums

Represent each number as the sum of two rational numbers. Use a number line to explain your answer.

1. −2.1

2. −5$\frac{2}{3}$

3. 4$\frac{7}{9}$

4. 5.8

5. −1$\frac{4}{7}$

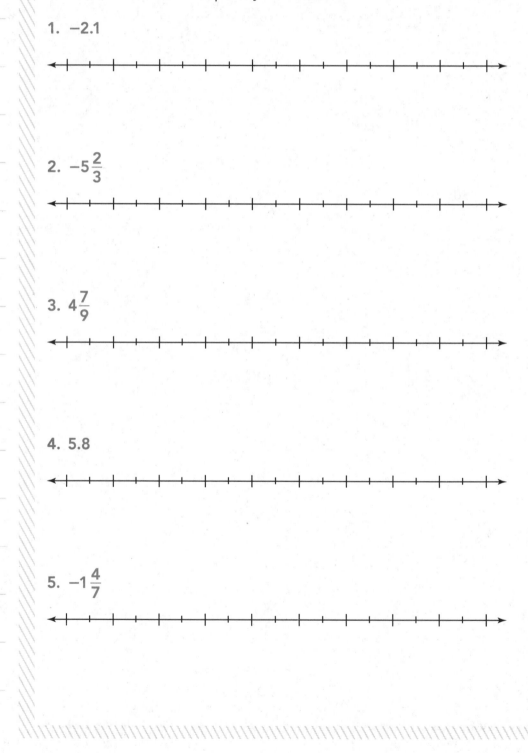

Assignment

Write

Explain in your own words how adding and subtracting positive and negative numbers with fractions and decimals is different from and similar to adding and subtracting with whole numbers.

Remember

The opposite of a number is called the additive inverse of the number. The absolute value of the difference between two numbers is a measure of the distance between the numbers.

Practice

Consider the subtraction expression $-1.3 - (-2.4)$.

1. Use a number line to solve the problem.
2. Use a two-color counter model to solve the problem.

Calculate each sum. Be sure to estimate first.

3. $12\frac{2}{5} + \left(-3\frac{1}{4}\right)$
4. $5.3 + (-7.45)$
5. $-\frac{5}{8} + 8\frac{3}{8}$

Calculate each difference. Estimate before calculating.

6. $-8.38 - 11.29$
7. $7\frac{2}{3} - \left(-4\frac{1}{4}\right)$
8. $-4\frac{5}{6} - 6\frac{2}{3}$

Stretch

Determine each solution. Let $-3 = x$, $-5 = y$, and $-4 = k$.

1. $|x - y - y - k + y + x|$
2. $k - y - k + x + k$
3. $-k - y + x - y$

Review

1. Determine each difference. Then, write a sentence that describes the movement on the number line that you could use to solve the problem.

   a. $7 - (-6)$

   b. $-5 - 13$

2. Shilo is riding her bicycle across the state of Georgia to raise money for her favorite charity. The distance in miles that she can travel varies directly with the length of time in hours she spends riding. Assume that her constant of proportionality is 18. What does the constant of proportionality represent in this problem?

3. The constant of proportionality between the number of children on a field trip and the number of teachers on the trip is $\frac{14}{3}$. There are 70 children on a field trip. How many teachers are on the trip?

4. Determine two unit rates for each given rate.

   a. 12 students ate 4.5 pizzas.

   b. Shae painted $\frac{1}{3}$ of the wall in $\frac{1}{4}$ hour.

Adding and Subtracting Rational Numbers Summary

KEY TERMS

- absolute value
- additive inverses
- zero pair

LESSON 1	Math Football

Combining positive and negative moves together on a line results in moving to the left, moving to the right, or staying in the same position, depending on the size of the positive and negative values. For example, the table shows possible moves in the game of Math Football.

	Player	Starting Position	Results of the Number Cubes Roll	Ending Position
First Turn	Home Team	0	Red 3 and Black 5	+2
	Visiting Team	0	Red 5 and Black 6	+1
Second Turn	Home Team	+2	Red 1 and Black 6	+7
	Visiting Team	+1	Red 6 and Black 2	−3

LESSON 2

Walk the Line

A number line can be used to model integer addition. When adding a positive integer, move to the right on a number line. When adding a negative integer, move to the left on a number line.

For example, this number line model shows how to determine 5 + (−8).

The **absolute value** of a number is its distance from 0. The absolute value of 5 is 5, and the absolute value of −8 is 8.

LESSON 3

Two-Color Counters

You can model the addition of integers using two-color counters that represent positive (+) charges and negative (−) charges.

The expression 3 + (−3) can be modeled in different ways.

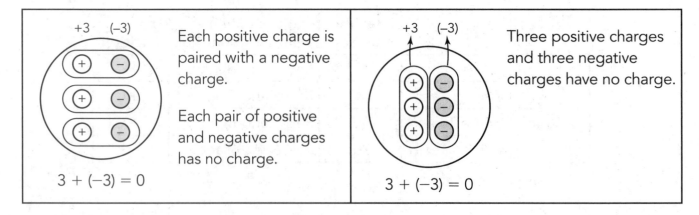

Two numbers with the sum of zero are called **additive inverses.** You can use additive inverses to model adding integers with different absolute values.

For example, the expression 5 + (−8) is modeled here using two-color counters. There are 3 negative charges remaining. The sum of 5 + (−8) is −3.

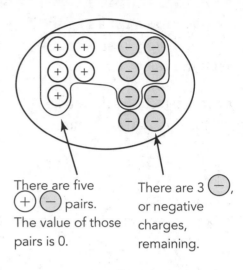

These are the rules for adding integers:

- When two integers have the same sign and are added together, the sign of the sum is the sign of both integers.

- When two integers have opposite signs and are added together, the absolute values of the integers are subtracted and the sign of the sum is the sign of the integer with the greater absolute value.

There are five
(+)(−) pairs.
The value of those
pairs is 0.

There are 3 (−),
or negative
charges,
remaining.

What's the Difference?

A number line can be used to model integer subtraction. When subtracting an integer, you move in the opposite direction.

For example, the number line model shows how to determine −6 − (+2).

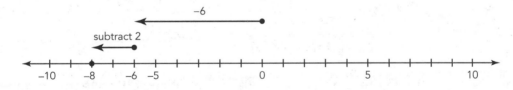

First, move to −6. Then, move in the opposite direction of adding (+2).

You can use two-color counters to model the subtraction of integers. To subtract integers using both positive and negative counters, you will need to use zero pairs. The value of a negative charge and a positive charge is zero, so together they form a **zero pair**.

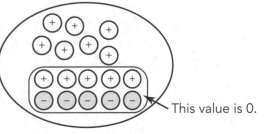

For example, the expression 7 − (−5) is modeled here using two-color counters.

This value is 0.

Start with 7 positive counters. There are no negative counters to subtract, so insert 5 negative counters into the model. You must also insert 5 positive counters in order not to change the value.

Now you can subtract, or take away, the 5 negative counters.

Take away 5 negative counters, and 12 positive counters remain.

$$7 - (-5) = 12$$

You can change any subtraction problem to an addition problem without changing the answer. Subtracting two integers is the same as adding the opposite of the subtrahend, the number you are subtracting.

LESSON 5 · All Mixed Up

You can use what you know about adding and subtracting integers to solve problems with positive and negative fractions and decimals.

For example, yesterday, Katrina was just $23.75 below her fundraising goal. She got a check today for $12.33 to put toward the fundraiser. Describe Katrina's progress toward the goal.

$$-\$23.75 + \$12.33 = -\$11.42$$

Katrina will still be below her goal, because $-11.42 < 0$.

The difference between two numbers is a measure of the distance between the numbers.

For example, the freezing point of chlorine is $-149.51°F$. The freezing point of zinc is $787.51°F$. How many more degrees is the freezing point of zinc than the freezing point of chlorine?

A model can help you estimate that the answer will be greater than 787.51.

$$787.51 - (-149.51) = 937.02$$

The freezing point of zinc is $937.02°F$ more than the freezing point of chlorine.

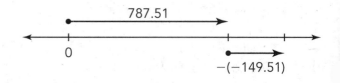

TOPIC 2
Multiplying and Dividing Rational Numbers

Multiplying and dividing are all about equal groups. Five each of four kinds of chocolate makes 20 total chocolates.

Lesson 1
Equal Groups
Multiplying and Dividing Integers M2-89

Lesson 2
Be Rational!
Quotients of Integers. M2-103

Lesson 3
Building a Wright Brothers' Flyer
Simplifying Expressions to Solve Problems M2-113

Lesson 4
Properties Schmoperties
Using Number Properties to Interpret Expressions with Signed Numbers M2-125

Module 2: Operating with Signed Numbers

TOPIC 2: MULTIPLYING AND DIVIDING RATIONAL NUMBERS

In this topic, students use number lines and two-color counters to model the multiplication of integers before developing rules for determining the product of signed numbers. Students use patterns and multiplication fact families to develop the rules for the quotient of signed numbers, namely that the same rules apply to quotients as products. After students understand multiplying and dividing integers, they apply the rules to the set of rational numbers in the context of problem solving.

Where have we been?

Students have learned to use number lines and two-color counters to represent and model operations with integers. Even earlier, in elementary school, students learned that multiplication can be viewed as repeated addition and as equal groups of objects. Fact families, a familiar concept from elementary school, are used to help students generalize the rules for the signs of the products and quotients.

Where are we going?

It is essential that students develop a strong conceptual foundation for multiplying and dividing with rational numbers, as a basis for manipulating and representing increasingly complex numeric and algebraic expressions. In high school, students will focus more on expressions and equations than on numbers, including rational expressions, equations, and functions.

Modeling Integer Products with Two-Color Counters and Number Lines

Both the number line and counter models represent the product $3 \times (-4)$, or 3 groups of -4.

Consider the expression $3 \times (-4)$. As repeated addition, it is represented as $(-4) + (-4) + (-4)$.

You can think of $3 \times (-4)$ as three groups of (-4).

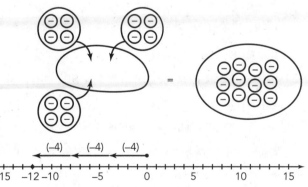

Myth: Just watch a video, and you will understand it.

Has this ever happened to you? Someone explains something, and it all makes sense at the time. You feel like you get it. But then, a day later when you try to do it on your own, you suddenly feel like something's missing? If that feeling is familiar, don't worry. It happens to us all. It's called the illusion of explanatory depth, and it frequently happens after watching a video.

How do you break this illusion? The first step is to try to make the video interactive. Don't treat it like a TV show. Instead, pause the video and try to explain it to yourself or to a friend. Alternatively, attempt the steps in the video on your own and rewatch it if you hit a wall. Remember, it's easy to confuse familiarity with understanding.

#mathmythbusted

Talking Points

You can further support your student's learning by asking questions about the work they do in class or at home. Your student is learning to multiply and divide with negative integers and rational numbers.

Questions to Ask

- How does this problem look like something you did in class?
- Can you show me the strategy you used to solve this problem? Do you know another way to solve it?
- Does your answer make sense? How do you know?
- Is there anything you don't understand? How can you use today's lesson to help?

Key Terms

terminating decimals
A terminating decimal has a finite number of digits, meaning that after a finite number of decimal places, all following decimal places have a value of 0.

repeating decimals
A repeating decimal is a decimal in which a digit or a group of digits repeat infinitely.

bar notation
Bar notation is used to indicate the digits that repeat in a repeating decimal. In the quotient of 1 and 7, the sequence 142857 repeats. The digits that lie underneath the bar are the digits that repeat.

$$\frac{1}{7} = 0.142857142857... = 0.\overline{142857}$$

Equal Groups

Multiplying and Dividing Integers

1

WARM UP

Determine each sum.

1. $-2\frac{3}{4} + \left(-2\frac{3}{4}\right)$

2. $-9.502 - 4.239$

3. $-3 + 8 + (-2)$

4. $5 - 16 + 7 + (-1)$

LEARNING GOALS

- Multiply integers using models.
- Develop rules for multiplying integers.
- Develop rules for dividing integers.

You know the reasoning and rules to add and subtract integers. How do you multiply and divide integers?

Addition or Multiplication?

Consider the addition problem $(-8) + (-8) + (-8) + (-8)$.

1. Rewrite the addition problem as a multiplication problem.

2. Is the product from Question 1 positive or negative? Explain your reasoning.

Consider the addition problem $(-1) + (-1) + (-1) + (-1) + (-1)$.

3. Rewrite the addition problem as a multiplication problem.

4. Is the product from Question 3 positive or negative? Explain your reasoning.

5. What relationship helped you answer Questions 2 and 4?

Modeling the Multiplication of Integers

When thinking about multiplying integers, remember that multiplication can be represented as repeated addition.

WORKED EXAMPLE 1

Consider the expression 3×4.

As repeated addition, it is representented as $4 + 4 + 4$.

You can think of 3×4 as three groups of 4.

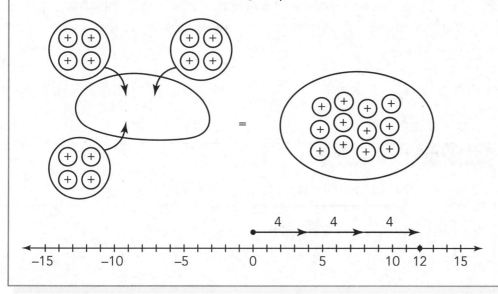

1. **Explain how the number line in Worked Example 1 illustrates 3×4.**

WORKED EXAMPLE 2

Consider the expression $3 \times (-4)$. As repeated addition, it is represented as $(-4) + (-4) + (-4)$.

You can think of $3 \times (-4)$ as three groups of (-4).

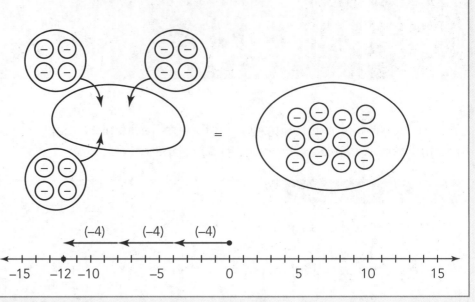

2. Explain how each model in Worked Example 2 can be interpreted as three groups of *the opposite of 4*.

WORKED EXAMPLE 3

Consider the expression $4 \times (-3)$.

How is the number line model similar to models you have used to add positive numbers?

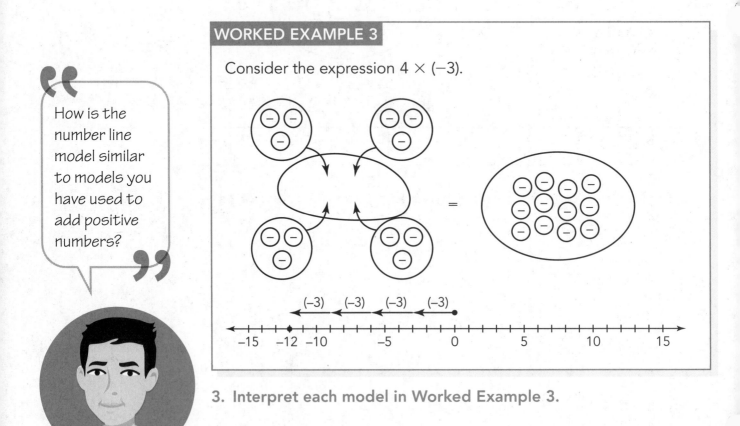

3. Interpret each model in Worked Example 3.

Consider the expression $(-3) \times (-4)$.

You know that $3 \times (-4)$ means "three groups of (-4)" and that -3 means "the opposite of 3." So, $(-3) \times (-4)$ means "the opposite of 3 groups of (-4)."

Think about how the 4 worked examples are alike and how they are different.

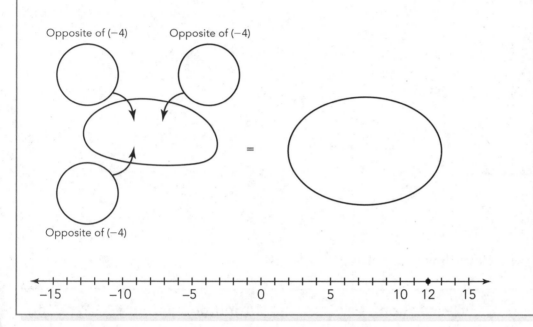

4. Complete the model by drawing in the appropriate counters and the appropriate rays in Worked Example 4.

   a. Determine the product and explain how your models illustrate this product.

   b. This expression can be written as $-((-4) + (-4) + (-4))$. Rewrite the expression as the opposite of a number: $-(\underline{\hspace{1cm}})$.

   c. How does the expression you wrote in part (b) relate to the product? Explain why this makes sense.

5. Draw either a number line or two-color counter model to
   determine each product. Describe the expression in words.

   a. 2 × 3

   b. 2 × (−3)

   c. (−2) × 3

   d. (−2) × (−3)

6. Complete the table.

Expression	Description	Addition Sentence	Product
3 × 5	Three groups of 5	5 + 5 + 5 = 15	15
(−3) × 5			
3 × (−5)			
(−3) × (−5)			

7. What do you notice about the products and their signs across
   the problems in this activity?

Signed Multiplication Facts

Analyze the sequence of products with 4.

1. What pattern do you notice in the products as the numbers multiplied by 4 decrease?

$4 \times 5 = 20$
$4 \times 4 = 16$
$4 \times 3 = 12$
$4 \times 2 = 8$
$4 \times 1 = 4$
$4 \times 0 = 0$

2. Continue the pattern to determine each product.

   a. $4 \times (-1) =$ _____   b. $4 \times (-2) =$ _____

   c. $4 \times (-3) =$ _____

3. Describe the pattern(s) that you notice in the new products.

Analyze the sequence of products with −5.

4. Describe the pattern and then extend it by writing the next three number sentences.

$-5 \times 5 = -25$
$-5 \times 4 = -20$
$-5 \times 3 = -15$
$-5 \times 2 = -10$
$-5 \times 1 = -5$
$-5 \times 0 = 0$

5. How do these products change as the numbers multiplied by −5 decrease?

Look back at the products you have determined in this lesson to answer each question.

6. Describe the sign of the product of two integers when:

   a. they are both positive.   b. they are both negative.

   c. one is positive and   d. one is zero.
      one is negative.

7. If you know that the product of two integers is negative, what can you say about the two integers? Give examples.

8. Describe a rule that will help you multiply any two integers.

Does the order in which you multiply the integers matter?

9. Use your rule to evaluate each expression.

   a.   6 × 5 = _____   b.   −8 × 7 = _____
            6 × (−5) = _____   −8 × (−7) = _____
           −6 × 5 = _____   8 × (−7) = _____
          −6 × (−5) = _____   8 × 7 = _____

   c.   −3 × 2 × (−4) = _____
          −3 × (−2) × (−4) = _____
            3 × (−2) × 4 = _____
          −3 × (−2) × 4 = _____
            3 × 2 × (−4) = _____
           −3 × 2 × 4 = _____

10. Describe the sign of each product and how you know.

Create some examples to test if you are not sure how to answer these questions.

a. the product of three negative integers

b. the product of four negative integers

c. the product of seven negative integers

d. the product of ten negative integers

11. What is the sign of the product of any odd number of negative integers? Explain your reasoning.

How is determining the sign of the product different from when you add and subtract signed numbers?

12. What is the sign of the product of three positive integers and five negative integers? Explain your reasoning.

ACTIVITY 1.3 | Signed Fact Families

When you studied division in elementary school, you learned that multiplication and division were inverse operations. For every multiplication fact, you can write a corresponding division fact.

WORKED EXAMPLE

Consider the fact family for 4, 5, and 20.

$$4 \times 5 = 20$$
$$5 \times 4 = 20$$
$$20 \div 4 = 5$$
$$20 \div 5 = 4$$

Similarly, you can write fact families for integer multiplication and division.

EXAMPLES:

$$-7 \times 3 = -21 \qquad\qquad -8 \times (-4) = 32$$
$$3 \times (-7) = -21 \qquad\qquad -4 \times (-8) = 32$$
$$-21 \div (-7) = 3 \qquad\qquad 32 \div (-8) = -4$$
$$-21 \div 3 = -7 \qquad\qquad 32 \div (-4) = -8$$

1. What pattern(s) do you notice in each fact family?

2. Write a fact family for −6, 8, and −48.

3. Fill in the unknown numbers to make each number sentence true.

Use fact families to help you determine each answer.

a. $56 \div (-8) = $ _____

b. $28 \div (-4) = $ _____

c. $-63 \div $ _____ $= -7$

d. $24 \div $ _____ $= -8$

e. _____ $\div (-8) = -4$

f. $-105 \div $ _____ $= -5$

g. _____ $\div (-8) = 0$

h. $-26 \div $ _____ $= -1$

4. Describe the sign of the quotient of two integers when:

a. both integers are positive.

b. one integer is positive and one integer is negative.

c. both integers are negative.

Remember that a quotient is the answer to a division problem.

d. the dividend is zero.

5. How do the answers to Question 4 compare to the answers to the same questions about the multiplication of two integers? Explain your reasoning.

TALK the TALK

What's Your Sign?

Think about patterns in the signs of sums, differences, products, and quotients of integers.

1. Determine two different sets of single-digit integers that make each number sentence true.

   a. ____ × ____ = −42   b. ____ × ____ = 56

   c. ____ × ____ = 63   d. ____ × ____ = −48

2. Complete the table by writing the sign (+, −, or +/−) to describe each sum, difference, product, or quotient.

Description of Integers	Addition (Sum)	Subtraction (Difference)	Multiplication (Product)	Division (Quotient)
two positive integers				
two negative integers				
one positive and one negative integer				

3. Create a true multiplication or division number sentence that meets the given condition.

   a. positive product   b. negative product

   c. positive quotient   d. negative quotient

Assignment

Write

Explain how you determine the sign of the product or quotient of three of integers.

Remember

To multiply and divide integers, perform the usual multiplication and division algorithms and then apply the correct sign to the product or quotient.

Practice

Draw a two-color counter model to determine each product. Describe the expression in words.

1. $6 \times (-3)$
2. -2×5
3. $-4 \times (-2)$

Complete a number line model to determine each product.

4. -2×7
5. $-5 \times (-3)$
6. $3 \times (-3)$

Determine each product.

7. 5×11
   $5 \times (-11)$
   -5×11
   $-5 \times (-11)$

8. $3 \times 4 \times 5$
   $-3 \times (-4) \times 5$
   $-3 \times 4 \times 5$
   $-3 \times (-4) \times (-5)$
   $3 \times 4 \times (-5)$
   $3 \times (-4) \times (-5)$

Determine the integer that makes each number sentence true.

9. _____ $\times (-9) = -36$

10. $3 \times$ _____ $= -24$

11. $14 \times$ _____ $= 56$

12. _____ $\times (-6) = 30$

13. $9 = (-63) \div$ _____

14. $-40 \div$ _____ $= -8$

15. $16 \div$ _____ $= -8$

16. _____ $\div (-6) = -4$

Stretch

Multiplication can be represented as repeated addition. Repeated multiplication leads to exponents. Use what you know about multiplying signed numbers to evaluate each expression.

1. $(-3)^3$

2. $(-4)^2$

3. $(-2)^5$

4. $\left(-\frac{1}{2}\right)^2$

What do you notice?

Review

1. The Baby Shop sells baby supplies for new families. They offer different brands of the same items. James and his mom are shopping for his new baby brother. It is James' job to make sure that his mom is making wise purchases. Their first item to purchase is diapers. There are 3 different options for newborn-sized diapers.

   Stay-Dry: 108 diapers for $25.18
   UberSoft: 180 diapers for $39.14
   Cuddlies: 160 diapers for $38.77

   a. What is a unit rate for the Stay-Dry diapers?
   b. What is a unit rate for the UberSoft diapers?
   c. What is a unit rate for the Cuddlies diapers?
   d. Which kind of diapers should James advise his mom to purchase?

2. Calculate each sum.

   a. $2\frac{1}{2} + \left(-3\frac{3}{4}\right) + 5\frac{2}{5}$

   b. $5\frac{1}{3} + \left(-4\frac{1}{6}\right) + \left(-2\frac{1}{2}\right)$

3. Determine each unit rate.

   a. $1\frac{1}{4}$ teaspoons baking powder per $\frac{3}{8}$ cup flour

   b. $2\frac{2}{5}$ parts ammonia per $1\frac{1}{3}$ parts vinegar

Be Rational! 2
Quotients of Integers

WARM UP

Classify each number into as many categories as it belongs: natural number, whole number, integer, rational number.

1. -3
2. $\frac{1}{2}$
3. 0
4. 5

LEARNING GOALS

- Know that the decimal form of a rational number terminates in 0s or eventually repeats.
- Represent rational numbers as terminating or repeating decimals.
- Use long division to represent quotients of integers as rational numbers.
- Write equivalent forms of signed rational numbers.
- Determine that every quotient of integers is a rational number, provided the divisor is not zero.

KEY TERMS

- terminating decimals
- non-terminating decimals
- repeating decimals
- bar notation
- non-repeating decimals

You have learned the rule to determine the sign of a quotient. Does a quotient change if the negative sign is on the divisor instead of the dividend?

Are You a Terminator?

1. For each pair of numbers, use long division to calculate the quotient. Write quotients in fractional and decimal form.

    a. $5 \div 8$ b. $5 \div 11$

    c. $7 \div 9$ d. $6 \div 2$

2. What types of numbers are the quotients in Question 1? Use the definitions of the different number classifications to explain why this makes sense.

3. How many decimal places did you need to go to in the long division for each quotient? Why?

Classifying Decimals

Decimals can be classified into two categories: *terminating* and *non-terminating*.

A **terminating decimal** has a finite number of digits, meaning that after a finite number of decimal places, all following decimal places have a value of 0. Terminating decimals are rational numbers.

A **non-terminating decimal** is a decimal that continues on infinitely without ending in a sequence of zeros.

1. Classify the decimals in Question 1 as terminating or non-terminating decimals.

2. Determine which unit fractions are terminating and which are non-terminating? Explain your reasoning for each.

$\frac{1}{2}$ $\frac{1}{3}$ $\frac{1}{4}$ $\frac{1}{5}$ $\frac{1}{6}$ $\frac{1}{7}$ $\frac{1}{8}$ $\frac{1}{9}$ $\frac{1}{10}$

Pi (π) is one of the most well-known non-repeating decimals.

Non-terminating decimals can be further divided into two categories: *repeating* and *non-repeating*.

A **repeating decimal** is a decimal in which a digit, or a group of digits, repeat(s) infinitely. Repeating decimals are rational numbers.

Bar notation is used to indicate the digits that repeat in a repeating decimal. In the quotient of 3 and 7, the sequence 428571 repeats. The numbers that lie underneath the bar are the numbers that repeat.

The bar is called a vinculum.

$$\frac{3}{7} = 0.4285714285714\ldots = 0.\overline{428571}$$

A **non-repeating decimal** continues without terminating and without repeating a sequence of digits. Non-repeating decimals are not rational numbers.

3. Classify the non-terminating decimals in Question 1 as repeating or non-repeating decimals. If they are repeating decimals, rewrite them using bar notation.

If you can find a counterexample to your conjecture, revise your conjecture.

4. Use your results in Question 2 to make a conjecture about other fractions. Which fractions will have repeating decimal representations? Use examples to support your conjecture.

Cut out the numbers at the end of the lesson. There are four possible representations of each rational number, but not all of the rational numbers have all four representations provided.

1. Sort the numbers into their equivalent representations. For any numbers that do not have four representations, create the missing representation using the blank cards. Tape or glue the sets of representations in the space provided.

Think about how you determine the sign of a quotient. What is special about each of these representations?

Consider how you can use positive and negative signs to write an equivalent form of $\frac{3}{5}$.

2. What do you notice about the negative sign in the fraction form of the representations?

TALK the TALK

It's All the Same to Me

Any quotient of two integers is a rational number, so long as the divisor is not 0.

For each rational number,

- write two equivalent representations in fractional form,
- convert to a decimal,
- classify the decimal as terminating or non-terminating and, if applicable, repeating or non-repeating.

1. $\dfrac{-11}{25}$ 2. $\dfrac{-1}{6}$

3. $\dfrac{27}{-50}$ 4. $\dfrac{-3}{7}$

$-\dfrac{2}{3}$	$\dfrac{-4}{5}$	$\dfrac{11}{-4}$	$\dfrac{-13}{15}$
$\dfrac{-39}{60}$	$\dfrac{-7}{22}$	$\dfrac{2}{-3}$	$-0.8\overline{6}$
$-\dfrac{11}{4}$	$\dfrac{4}{-5}$	$\dfrac{13}{-15}$	$-0.\overline{6}$
$-\dfrac{39}{60}$	$\dfrac{7}{-22}$	$\dfrac{-2}{3}$	$-\dfrac{4}{5}$

Assignment

Write

Explain how the three different fractional representations of a rational number are related to determining the sign of the quotient of two integers.

Remember

The sign of a negative rational number in fractional form can be placed in front of the fraction, in the numerator of the fraction, or in the denominator of the fraction.

Practice

Convert each fraction to a decimal. Classify the decimal as *terminating*, *non-terminating*, *repeating*, or *non-repeating*. If the decimal repeats, rewrite it using bar notation.

1. $\frac{3}{8}$
2. $\frac{5}{6}$
3. $\frac{7}{25}$
4. $\frac{2}{11}$
5. $\frac{5}{12}$

Write each rational number as an equivalent fraction by changing the placement of the negative sign(s).

6. $-\frac{4}{7}$
7. $\frac{-5}{3}$
8. $\frac{1}{2}$
9. $\frac{9}{-2}$
10. $-\frac{8}{5}$

Stretch

Use what you know about multiplying signed numbers to evaluate each expression.

1. $\left(-\frac{1}{2}\right)^2$
2. $-\left(\frac{1}{2}\right)^2$
3. $\left(-\frac{1}{2}\right)^3$
4. $-\left(\frac{1}{2}\right)^3$

What do you notice?

Review

Represent each scenario as a multiplication or division problem. Then, solve the problem.

1. The temperature changed −2° per hour for 5 hours. How many degrees did the temperature drop during that time period.

2. Lina missed 8 questions on her science final, which changed her final score by −32 points. If each question is weighted equally, how many points did she lose for each question?

Determine each product.

3. $2\frac{1}{2} \times \left(-3\frac{3}{4}\right)$

4. $-5\frac{1}{3} \times \left(-2\frac{1}{2}\right)$

Determine an 18% gratuity for each restaurant bill.

5. $29.50

6. $56.70

Building a Wright Brothers' Flyer

Simplifying Expressions to Solve Problems

WARM UP

Simplify each expression.

1. $-20 \div 2\left(7\frac{2}{3}\right)$

2. $-20 - 2\left(-7\frac{2}{3}\right)$

3. $-7\left(\dfrac{-\frac{3}{4}}{-\frac{2}{3}}\right)$

LEARNING GOALS

- Model situations using expressions with rational numbers.
- Evaluate expressions with rational numbers and variables.
- Solve real-world problems using operations with signed rational numbers.

KEY TERM

- percent error

You have learned how to operate with signed numbers, including integers and other rational numbers. How can you use what you know to solve problems?

Orville and Wilbur

In the middle of December 1903, two brothers—Orville and Wilbur Wright—became the first two people to make a controlled flight in a powered plane. They made four flights on December 17, the longest covering only 852 feet and lasting just 59 seconds.

The table shows information about the flights made that day.

	Pilot	Flight Time (s)	Distance (ft)
A	Orville	12	120
B	Wilbur	13	175
C	Orville	15	200
D	Wilbur	59	852

1. **Determine the approximate speed of all four flights, in miles per hour.**

Human flight progressed amazingly quickly after those first flights. In the year before Orville Wright died, Chuck Yeager had already piloted the first flight that went faster than the speed of sound: 767.269 miles per hour!

2. **What is the speed of sound in feet per second?**

Operating with Rational Numbers to Solve Problems

In order to build a balsa wood model of the Wright brothers' plane, you would need to cut long lengths of wood spindles into shorter lengths for the wing stays, the vertical poles that support and connect the two wings. Each stay for the main wings of the model needs to be cut $3\frac{1}{4}$ inches long.

Show your work and explain your reasoning.

1. If the wood spindles are each 10 inches long, how many stays could you cut from one spindle?

2. How many inches of the spindle would be left over?

3. If the wood spindles are each 12 inches long, how many stays could you cut from one spindle?

4. How many inches of the spindle would be left over?

You also need to cut vertical stays for the smaller wing that are each $1\frac{5}{8}$ inches long.

5. If the wood spindles are each 10 inches long, how many of these stays could you cut from one spindle?

6. How many inches of the spindle would be left over?

7. If the wood spindles are each 12 inches long, how many stays could you cut from one spindle?

8. How many inches of the spindle would be left over?

9. Which length of spindle should be used to cut each of the different stays so that there is the least amount wasted?

There are longer spindles that measure 36 inches.

1. How much of a 36-inch-long spindle would be left over if you cut one of the stays from it?

Remember, a stay is $3\frac{1}{4}$ inch.

2. How much of this spindle would be left over if you cut two of the stays from it?

3. Define variables and write and equation for the number of $3\frac{1}{4}$-inch stays and the amount of the 36-inch spindle left over.

4. Use your equation to calculate the amount of the spindle left over after cutting 13 stays.

Airline travel has come a long way since the days of Orville and Wilbur Wright. In 2015, there were approximately 9.1 million flights that took off from U.S. airports carrying approximately 895.5 million passengers. To transport this many passengers to and from their destinations, airlines have to make good estimations about the number of flights passengers will book, the size of the airplanes to use for a given route, and the approximate arrival time for each flight.

Tracking the accuracy of these estimations is important for airlines. Calculating **percent error** is one way to compare an estimated value to an actual value. To compute percent error, determine the difference between the estimated and actual values and then divide by the actual value.

$$\text{Percent Error} = \frac{\text{actual value} - \text{estimated value}}{\text{actual value}}$$

When planning which airplanes to use for a given route, airlines have to estimate how many people they think will book that particular flight. They want to be able to have enough seating to meet the demand but not have too big of a plane and waste the extra fuel needed.

1. An airline estimates that they will need an airplane that sits 224 passengers for the 6 A.M. flight from Washington, D.C., to Boston. Calculate the percent error for each number of actual passengers booked. Show your work.

   a. 186 booked tickets

   b. 250 booked tickets

Another challenge is accurately estimating the travel time for each flight. Having minimal error in these estimations allows airlines to keep their schedules accurate and passengers happy.

Airlines use historical data on how long the flight has taken in the past, but these estimates are often impacted by weather issues, airport traffic, and earlier flight delays.

2. An airline estimates that the flight from Washington, D.C., to Boston takes 1 hour and 27 minutes. Calculate the percent error for each actual flight time. Show your work.

   a. 1 hour and 11 minutes

   b. 2 hours

3. What does a negative value for percent error indicate?

4. Vernice is told that the DC to Boston flight took 10 minutes longer than estimated. She calculated the percent error and got 10.3%. She later learns that she had been given the wrong information. The flight took 10 minutes *less* than estimated. Vernice thinks that the percent error should just be −10.3%. Is she correct? Explain why or why not.

Evaluating Expressions with Rational Numbers and Variables

Recall that to evaluate an expression with a variable, substitute the value for the variable and then perform the operations.

WORKED EXAMPLE

Evaluate the expression $-12\frac{1}{2} - 3v$ for $v = -5$.

Estimate:

$$-12 - 3(-5) = -12 + 15 = 3$$

Substitute -5 for v and solve:

$$-12\frac{1}{2} - 3(-5) = -12\frac{1}{2} - (-15)$$

$$= -12\frac{1}{2} + 15$$

$$= 2\frac{1}{2}$$

1. **Evaluate the expression for $v = -\frac{6}{7}$.**

Evaluate each expression for the given value.

2. Evaluate $-3.25 - 2.75z$ for $z = -4$.

3. Evaluate $\left(-1\frac{1}{4}\right)x - 8\frac{7}{8}$ for $x = -\frac{2}{5}$.

4. Evaluate $-0.75(p - 1.2)$ for $p = 2$.

I'll TRY to remember to check my work. How can I do that?

5. Evaluate $\dfrac{m}{-\frac{6}{5}}$ for $m = 6\frac{3}{4}$.

TALK the TALK

Rational Thinking

Write each problem as a product or quotient of rational numbers and then solve. Show your work.

1. Carey and Patrick both borrowed money from Melinda. Carey owes Melinda $25.00. Patrick owes Melinda $\frac{3}{4}$ the amount that Carey owes. How much does Patrick owe Melinda?

2. Therese is measuring how fast water evaporates in a bucket in her backyard. In 6 hours in direct sunlight, the water level changes $-\frac{3}{8}$ inch. How fast is the water level changing per hour?

3. A meteorologist forecasts that the temperature is going to change $-1\frac{1}{2}°$ per hour from 11:00 P.M. to 7:00 A.M. What is the total expected temperature change over the time period?

Assignment

Write

Write the steps you would follow to evaluate an expression for a variable. Use an example in your description.

Remember

Percent error is one way to report the difference between estimated values and actual values.

$$\text{Percent error} = \frac{\text{actual value} - \text{estimated value}}{\text{actual value}}$$

Practice

Write an expression with rational numbers to represent each situation and then solve. Show your work.

1. Jaxon's start-up business makes a profit of $450 during the first month. However, the company records a profit of −$60 per month for the next four months and profit of $125 for the final month. What is the total profit for the first six months of Jaxon's business?

2. A diver is exploring the waters of the Great Barrier Reef.

   a. She is currently −5 feet from the surface of the water and plans to explore a shipwreck that is at −75 feet from the surface. If she moves at a rate of −8 feet per minute, how many minutes does it take the diver to reach the shipwreck?

   b. When she is done exploring the reef, she ascends at a rate of 5 feet per minute. Once she reaches a height of −30 feet, she must rest for 15 minutes to allow her body to adapt to the changing water pressure. She then continues to the surface at the same rate. How long will it take the diver to reach the surface?

3. The drain in your 45-gallon bathtub is partially clogged, but you need to take a shower. The showerhead had a flow rate of 2.25 gallons per minute, but the bathtub only drains at a rate of −0.5 gallons per minute. What is the longest shower you can take?

4. Tesha withdrew $22.75 each week for four weeks from her savings account to pay for her piano lessons. By how much did these lessons change her savings account balance?

Calculate the percent error.

5. Jerri estimated that 30 people would attend the dinner event, but only 25 people attended.

6. Gene estimated the length of the fence to be 150 feet, but the actual measurement was 142 feet.

Evaluate each expression for the given value.

7. $\frac{5}{6}x$ for $x = -8$

8. $9\frac{1}{3} - m$ for $m = -1\frac{2}{3}$

9. $t \div \frac{3}{4}$ for $t = 9\frac{3}{4}$

10. $\frac{2}{5}k - 3\frac{1}{2}$ for $k = 15$

Stretch

Solve each equation.

1. $x + 4.5 = 9.125$

2. $\frac{4}{5}(p + 1) = 1$

3. $\frac{g}{8} - 5 = 1\frac{1}{2}$

Review

Convert each fraction to a decimal. Classify the decimal as terminating or non-terminating and, if applicable, repeating or non-repeating.

1. $\frac{11}{12}$

2. $\frac{11}{14}$

Determine each absolute value. Show your work.

3. $|-5 - (-7)|$

4. $\left|-\frac{3}{8} + \frac{1}{6}\right|$

Determine each quotient.

5. $\frac{3}{4} \div \frac{4}{3}$

6. $\frac{1}{8} \div \frac{1}{5}$

Properties Schmoperties

Using Number Properties to Interpret Expressions with Signed Numbers

WARM UP

Use the Order of Operations to simplify each expression.

1. $18 + 6 \times (-3) - 4$

2. $5 \div (1 - 6) \times 10$

3. $8 + (-3) \times 9 \times 0$

LEARNING GOALS

- Use the Commutative, Associative, and Distributive Properties, Additive and Multiplicative Inverses, Identity, and Zero Properties to rewrite numeric expressions with signed numbers in order to interpret their meanings and solve problems.
- Apply the properties of operations to add, subtract, multiply, and divide with rational numbers.
- Use number properties to solve mathematical problems involving signed numbers and other rational numbers more efficiently.

You have learned how to add, subtract, multiply, and divide with signed numbers and other rational numbers. How can you use number properties with rational numbers to solve problems?

All in Your Head

You have used mental math before to solve problems without calculating on paper. Now try it with signed numbers!

1. Determine each sum or difference using mental math.

    a. $-8 + 5 + 8$

    b. $-\dfrac{1}{2} + \dfrac{3}{5} + -\dfrac{1}{2}$

    c. $\dfrac{3}{8} + \left(\dfrac{5}{8} + \left(-\dfrac{5}{6} \right) \right)$

The Commutative Property says that you can add or multiply in any order without changing the sum or product.

The Associative Property says that you can group addends or factors without changing the sum or product.

2. **Explain how you can use the Commutative and Associative Properties to help you solve the problems in your head.**

ACTIVITY 4.1

Distributing and Factoring with −1

When first learning about negative numbers, you reflected a positive value across 0 to determine the opposite of the value.

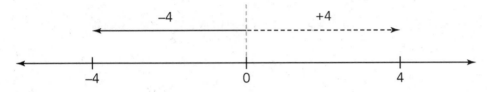

This illustrates that the opposite of 4 is −4, or $(-1)(4) = -4$.

In the same way, you can use reflections across 0 on the number line to determine the opposite of an expression.

WORKED EXAMPLE

Consider the expression $-7 + 2$. When the model of $-7 + 2$ is reflected across 0 on the number line, the result is $7 - 2$.

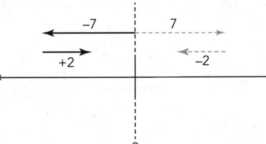

So, $(-7 + 2)$ is the opposite of $(7 - 2)$.

This means that $-7 + 2 = -(7 - 2)$.

---

1. **Draw models like the ones in the worked example to show the opposite of each expression. Rewrite each as an opposite of a different expression.**

   a. $-1 - 6$ b. $2 + (-3)$ c. $-4 + 5$

How would your answer be different if the expression were -4×5?

Adam

👍

To reflect an expression across 0 on the number line, multiply the expression by -1.

$$-1(2 + 3) = (-1)(2) + (-1)(3)$$
$$= -2 + -3$$

2. What property did Adam use to show his reasoning?

3. Does Adam's expression, $-1(2 + 3)$, mean the same thing as $-(2 + 3)$? Draw a model and explain your reasoning.

Rewriting an expression as a product with −1 is also called *factoring out a −1*.

4. Rewrite each expression as an addition or subtraction expression using a factor of −1.

   a. $-2 + (-4) = -1(\rule{2cm}{0.4pt})$

   b. $-5 - 8 = -1(\rule{2cm}{0.4pt})$

   c. $-9 - (-9) = -1(\rule{2cm}{0.4pt})$

5. Use the Distributive Property to show that your expressions in Question 4 are correct.

Subtraction as Adding the Opposite

You know that subtracting a number is the same as adding the opposite of that number. Rewriting subtraction as addition allows you to apply the Commutative Property to any expression involving addition and subtraction.

For example, $-4.5 - 3 + 1.5 = -4.5 + 1.5 + (-3)$. Rewriting expressions helps you to see patterns and use mental math to make solving simpler.

You can use what you know about adding opposites to help you solve problems more efficiently.

> You can rewrite a mixed number as the sum of a whole number and a fraction.
> $7\frac{1}{2} = 7 + \frac{1}{2}$
> How can you rewrite $-7\frac{1}{2}$?

1. Simplify each expression.

   a. $10.5 + 6 + 2 - 0.5$

   b. $-\frac{1}{2} + \left(\frac{1}{2} - \frac{4}{5}\right)$

   c. $3\frac{7}{8} - 4\frac{1}{2}$

2. Explain how you can use the Commutative, Associative, and Distributive Properties to help you simplify the expressions in Question 1.

ACTIVITY 4.3 Practice with the Properties

1. For each equation, identify the number property or operation used.

Equation   **Number Property**

a. $-3\frac{1}{2} + 5 = 5 + \left(-3\frac{1}{2}\right)$

b. $\left(3\frac{1}{2}\right)\left(2\frac{1}{5}\right)5 = 3\frac{1}{2}\left(2\frac{1}{5}\right)(5)$

c. $-3\frac{1}{2} + \left(-2\frac{1}{2} + 5\right) = \left(-3\frac{1}{2} + \left(-2\frac{1}{2}\right)\right) + 5$

d. $-\left(-3\frac{1}{2} + 2\frac{1}{4}\right) = -1\left(-3\frac{1}{2}\right) + -1\left(2\frac{1}{4}\right)$

e. $\dfrac{-3\frac{1}{2} - 2\frac{1}{4}}{4} = \dfrac{-3\frac{1}{2}}{4} - \dfrac{2\frac{1}{4}}{4}$

f. $(-7.02)(-3.42) = (-3.42)(-7.02)$

Evaluate each expression. Describe your strategy.

2. $-2\left(2\frac{1}{4}\right) + -2\left(-\frac{3}{4}\right)$

3. $\left(-3\frac{1}{4} - 2\frac{1}{5}\right) + \left(-6\frac{3}{5}\right)$

4. $\frac{7}{8}\left(-\frac{4}{5}\right)\left(-\frac{8}{7}\right)$

5. $\dfrac{\frac{8}{9} + \left(-\frac{4}{5}\right)}{4}$

6. $(-11.4)(6.4) + (-11.4)(-12.4)$

TALK the TALK

What's It All About?

When you rewrite addition and subtraction expressions using a factor of −1, you are "factoring out" a −1. Here are some other examples.

$$-8 + 5 = -1(8 - 5) \qquad -2 - 9 = -1(2 + 9) \qquad 3 - (-4) = -1(-3 - 4)$$

1. Describe how you can factor out a −1 from any addition or subtraction expression.

2. How is factoring out a negative 1 from an addition or subtraction expression different from factoring out a negative 1 from a multiplication or division expression?

3. Demonstrate using words and models why the product of −1 and any expression is the opposite of that expression.

Assignment

Write

Describe in your own words how to factor a −1 out of an addition or subtraction expression.

Remember

When you multiply any expression by −1, the result is the opposite of that expression.

Practice

Factor out a negative 1 from each expression.

1. 7 + (−6)
2. −4 − (5 + 3)
3. −9 − 1
4. Use the Distributive Property to show that your answers to Questions 1 through 3 are correct.

Use a number property to solve each problem efficiently. Show your work and list the property or properties used.

5. −9.9 + 5.2 + 3.9 + 1

6. $-\frac{3}{5} + \left(\frac{1}{5} - \frac{3}{2} + 0\right)$

Stretch

The rectangle shown is formed by a reflection of points C and D across the y-axis of the coordinate plane. Point C has the coordinates (4, 4). Determine a and b and then calculate the perimeter of the rectangle.

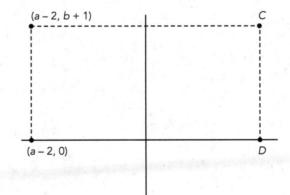

Review

1. Carl and Joe recorded how fast they ran 1 mile and 2 miles. Carl recorded his times using fractions, and Joe recorded his times using decimals.

Distance	Carl	Joe
1 mi	$10\frac{1}{2}$ min	10.4 min
2 mi	$22\frac{1}{4}$ min	22.3 min

   a. Who ran the mile faster, Carl or Joe? How much faster?

   b. Who ran 2 miles faster, Carl or Joe? How much faster?

2. A small submarine is at an elevation of -30 feet compared to sea level. What is its elevation after it ascends 9 feet?

3. On Tuesday, Marissa was $45 short of her fundraising goal. The next day, she was $5 over her goal. Write an equation to show how much she raised in one day.

4. What is 12% of 350?

5. What is 35% of 120?

Multiplying and Dividing Rational Numbers Summary

KEY TERMS

- terminating decimals
- non-terminating decimals
- repeating decimals
- bar notation
- non-repeating decimals
- percent error

LESSON 1 — Equal Groups

When thinking about multiplying integers, remember that you can think about multiplication like repeated addition.

For example, consider the expression $3 \times (-4)$. As repeated addition, it is represented as $(-4) + (-4) + (-4)$.

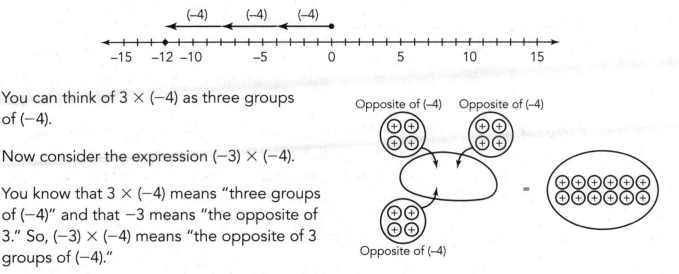

You can think of $3 \times (-4)$ as three groups of (-4).

Now consider the expression $(-3) \times (-4)$.

You know that $3 \times (-4)$ means "three groups of (-4)" and that -3 means "the opposite of 3." So, $(-3) \times (-4)$ means "the opposite of 3 groups of (-4)."

To multiply and divide integers, perform the usual multiplication and division algorithms, and then apply the correct sign to the product or quotient. An odd number of negative signs in the expression gives a negative product or quotient. An even number of negative signs in the expression gives a positive product or quotient.

When you studied division in elementary school, you learned that multiplication and division were inverse operations. For every multiplication fact, you can write a corresponding division fact. Similarly, you can write fact families for integer multiplication and division.

For example, consider these two fact families.

$$-7 \times 3 = -21 \qquad\qquad -8 \times (-4) = 32$$
$$3 \times (-7) = -21 \qquad\qquad -4 \times (-8) = 32$$
$$-21 \div (-7) = 3 \qquad\qquad 32 \div (-8) = -4$$
$$-21 \div 3 = -7 \qquad\qquad 32 \div (-4) = -8$$

LESSON
2

Be Rational!

Decimals can be classified into two categories: terminating and non-terminating. A **terminating decimal** has a finite number of digits, meaning that after a finite number of decimal places, all following decimal places have a value of 0. A **non-terminating decimal** is a decimal that continues infinitely, without ending in a sequence of zeros.

For example, 0.375 is a terminating decimal. The decimal 0.454545… is a non-terminating decimal.

Non-terminating decimals can be further divided into two categories: repeating and non-repeating.

A **repeating decimal** is a decimal in which a digit or a group of digits repeat infinitely. **Bar notation** is used to indicate the digit or digits that repeat in a repeating decimal. For example, in the quotient of 3 and 7, the sequence 428571 repeats. The digits that lie underneath the bar are the digits that repeat. Repeating decimals are rational numbers.

$$\frac{3}{7} = 0.4285714285714\ldots = 0.\overline{428571}$$

A **non-repeating decimal** continues without terminating and without repeating a sequence of digits. Non-repeating decimals are not rational numbers.

The sign of a negative rational number in fractional form can be placed in front of the fraction, in the numerator of the fraction, or in the denominator of the fraction.

$$-\frac{3}{5} = \frac{-3}{5} = \frac{3}{-5}$$

LESSON
3

Building a Wright Brothers' Flyer

You can use the rules you have learned to operate with rational numbers in order to solve problems and equations.

Percent error is one way to report the difference between estimated values and actual values.

$$\text{Percent error} = \frac{\text{actual value} - \text{estimated value}}{\text{actual value}}$$

For example, an airline estimates that they will need an airplane that sits 416 passengers for the 8 A.M. flight from Austin to Orlando. Calculate the percent error if 380 actual passengers are booked.

$$\frac{380-416}{380} = \frac{-36}{430} \approx -9.5\%$$

The airline served 9.5% fewer passengers than they expected.

Expressions with variables can be evaluated for rational numbers.

For example, evaluate the expression $-12\frac{1}{2} - 3v$ for $v = -5$.

Substitute -5 for v and solve:

$$-12\frac{1}{2} - 3(-5) = -12\frac{1}{2} - (-15)$$

$$= -12\frac{1}{2} + 15$$

$$= 2\frac{1}{2}$$

When $v = -5$, the value of the expression is $2\frac{1}{2}$.

Properties Schmoperties

You can use reflections across 0 on the number line to determine the opposite of an expression.

For example, consider the expression $-7 + 2$. When the model of $-7 + 2$ is reflected across 0 on the number line, the result is $7 - 2$.

Therefore, $(-7 + 2)$ is the opposite of $(7 - 2)$.

This means that $-7 + 2 = -(7 - 2)$.

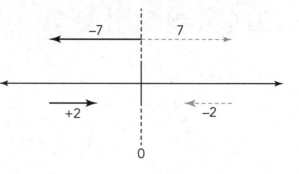

When you multiply any expression by -1, the result is the opposite of that expression.

Using number properties can help you to solve problems involving signed numbers more efficiently.

Rewriting subtraction as addition allows you apply the Commutative Property to any expression involving addition and subtraction. For example, $-4.5 - 3 + 1.5 = -4.5 + 1.5 + (-3)$.

You can apply what you know about the Zero Property of Addition and the Associative Property to expressions with positive and negative integers. For example, $-\frac{3}{4} + \left(\frac{3}{4} - \frac{1}{5}\right) = \left(-\frac{3}{4} + \frac{3}{4}\right) - \frac{1}{5} = 0 - \frac{1}{5} = -\frac{1}{5}$.

Glossary

absolute value

The absolute value, or magnitude, of a number is its distance from zero on a number line.

Example

The absolute value of −3 is the same as the absolute value of 3 because they are both a distance of 3 from zero on a number line.

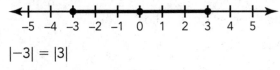

$|{-3}| = |3|$

additive inverses

Two numbers with the sum of zero are called additive inverses.

Examples

$-19 + 19 = 0$ $a + -a = 0$

adjacent angles

Adjacent angles are two angles that share a common vertex and share a common side.

Examples

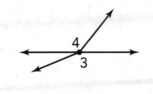

Angles 1 and 2 are adjacent angles.

Angles 3 and 4 are NOT adjacent angles.

algebraic expression

An algebraic expression is a mathematical phrase that has at least one variable, and it can contain numbers and operation symbols.

Examples

a $2a + b$ xy $\dfrac{4}{P}$ z^2

angle

An angle is formed by two rays that share a common endpoint.

Example

A

appreciation

Appreciation is an increase in price or value.

arc

An arc is the curve between two points on a circle.

Example

Arc AB is shown.

--- B ---

bar notation

Bar notation is used to indicate the digits that repeat in a repeating decimal.

Example

In the quotient of 3 and 7, the sequence 428571 repeats. The numbers that lie underneath the bar are the numbers that repeat.

$\frac{3}{7} = 0.4285714285714... = 0.\overline{428571}$

--- C ---

census

A census is the data collected from every member of a population.

Example

The U.S. Census is taken every 10 years. The U.S. government counts every member of the population every 10 years.

circle

A circle is a collection of points on the same plane equidistant from the same point. The center of a circle is the point from which all points on the circle are equidistant. Circles are named by their center point.

Example

The circle shown is Circle O.

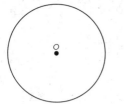

circumference

The distance around a circle is called the circumference of the circle. The circumference is calculated by the formula: $C = \pi(d)$.

Example

The diameter of Circle O is 12 centimeters. The circumference of Circle O is 12π.

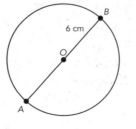

coefficient

A number that is multiplied by a variable in an algebraic expression is called a coefficient.

Examples

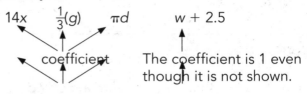

$14x \qquad \frac{1}{3}(g) \qquad \pi d \qquad w + 2.5$

coefficient

The coefficient is 1 even though it is not shown.

collinear

When points lie on the same line or line segment, they are said to be collinear.

Example

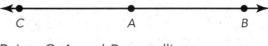

C   A   B

Points C, A, and B are collinear.

commission

A **commission** is an amount of money a salesperson earns after selling a product. Many times, the commission is a certain percent of the product.

Example

5% commission on $350

$0.05 \times 350 = \$17.50$ ◄— commission

common factor

A common factor is a number that is a factor of two or more numbers.

Example

factors of 60: **1, 2, 3, 4**, 5, **6**, 10, **12**, 15, 20, 30, 60

factors of 24: **1, 2, 3, 4, 6**, 8, **12**, 24

common factors of 60 and 24: 1, 2, 3, 4, 6, and 12

compass

A compass is a tool used to create arcs and circles.

complementary angles

Two angles are complementary angles if the sum of their angle measures is equal to 90°.

Example

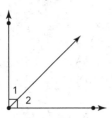

Angles 1 and 2 are complementary angles.

complementary events

Complementary events are events that together contain all of the outcomes in the sample space.

Example

When rolling a six-sided number cube with the numbers 1 through 6 on each face, the event of rolling an even number and the event of rolling an odd number (not even) are complementary events.

complex ratio

A ratio in which one or both of the quantities being compared are written as fractions is a complex ratio.

Example

Traveling $\frac{1}{3}$ mile in $\frac{1}{2}$ hour represents a ratio of fractions, or a complex ratio.

compound event

A compound event combines two or more events, using the word "and" or the word "or."

congruent

Congruent means to have the same size, shape, and measure.

Example

Square *ABCD* is congruent to Square *QRST*.

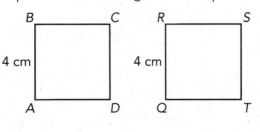

constant of proportionality

In a proportional relationship, the ratio of all y-values to their corresponding x-values is constant. This specific ratio, $\frac{y}{x}$, is called the constant of proportionality. Generally, the variable k is used to represent the constant of proportionality.

constraint

A constraint is a condition that a solution or problem must satisfy. A constraint can be a restriction set in advance of solving a problem or a limit placed on a solution or graph so the answer makes sense in terms of a real-world scenario.

Example

The expressions 0, x, 2x, −x, and −2x are graphed on a number line using the constraint $x < 0$.

constructions

Constructions are created using only a compass or a straightedge or both.

corresponding

Corresponding means to have the same relative position in geometric figures, usually referring to sides and angles.

Example

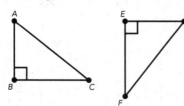

Sides *AB* and *DE* are corresponding sides.

Angle *B* and Angle *E* are corresponding angles.

cross-section

A cross-section of a solid is the two-dimensional figure formed by the intersection of a plane and a solid when a plane passes through the solid.

Example

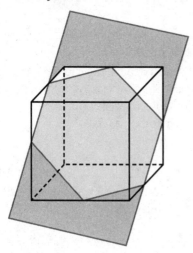

When a plane intersects a cube through all six faces, the cross-section is a hexagon.

D

data

Data are categories, numbers, or observations gathered in response to a statistical question.

Examples

favorite foods of sixth graders,
heights of different animals at the zoo

depreciation

Depreciation is a decrease in price or value

diameter

The diameter of a circle is a line segment formed by connecting two points on the circle such that the line segment passes through the center point.

Example

In Circle *O*, segment *AB* is a diameter. The length of diameter *AB* is two times the length of radius *OA*. The length of radius *OA* is 6 centimeters, so the length of diameter *AB* is 12 centimeters.

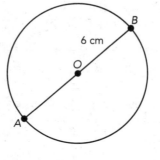

direct variation

A situation represents a direct variation if the ratio between the *y*-value and its corresponding *x*-value is constant for every point. The quantities are said to vary directly.

Example

If Melissa earns $8.25 per hour, then the amount she earns is in direct variation with the number of hours she works. The amount $8.25 is the constant of proportionality.

draw

When you draw a geometric figure, the figure is created with the use of tools such as a straightedge and protractor.

— E —

endpoints

The endpoints of a line segment are the points where the line segment ends. A line segment is named using the two capital letters that name its endpoints.

Example

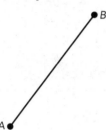

The endpoints A and B name line segment AB.

equally likely

When the probabilities of all the outcomes of an experiment are equal, then the outcomes are called equally likely.

Example

When rolling a six-sided number cube with the numbers 1 through 6 on each face, the probability of rolling each number from 1 through 6 is equally likely.

equation

An equation is a mathematical sentence that uses an equals sign to show that two quantities are the same as one another.

Examples

$$y = 2x + 4$$
$$6 = 3 + 3$$
$$2(8) = 26 - 10$$
$$\frac{1}{4} \cdot 4 = \frac{8}{4} - \frac{4}{4}$$

evaluate an algebraic expression

To evaluate an algebraic expression means to determine the value of the expression for a given value of each variable.

Example

Evaluate the expression $\frac{4x + (2^3 - y)}{p}$ for $x = 2.5$, $y = 8$, and $p = 2$.

- First replace the variables with numbers: $\frac{4(2.5) + (2^3 - 8)}{2}$.
- Then calculate the value of the expression: $\frac{10 + 0}{2} = \frac{10}{2} = 5$.

event

An event is one possible outcome or a group of possible outcomes for a given situation.

Example

When rolling a six-sided number cube with the numbers 1 through 6 on each face, an event could be rolling an even number.

experiment

An experiment is a situation involving chance that leads to results, or outcomes.

Example

Rolling a six-sided number cube is an experiment.

experimental probability

Experimental probability is the ratio of the number of times an event occurs to the total number of trials performed.

Example

Suppose there is one red, one blue, one green, and one yellow marble in a jar. You draw the blue marble 20 times out of 50 trials. The experimental probability, $P_E(\text{blue})$, is $\frac{20}{25}$ or $\frac{2}{5}$.

extremes

In a proportion that is written $a : b = c : d$, the two values on the outside, a and d, are the extremes.

Example

7 books : 14 days = 3 books : 6 days

extremes

F

factor

To factor an expression means to rewrite the expression as a product of factors.

Example

$5(12) + 5(9) = 5(12 + 9)$

G

greatest common factor (GCF)

The greatest common factor, or GCF, is the largest factor two or more numbers have in common.

Example

factors of 16: **1**, **2**, **4**, 8, 16

factors of 12: **1**, **2**, 3, **4**, 6, 12

common factors: 1, 2, 4

greatest common factor: 4

I

included angle

An included angle is the angle whose sides are made up of the given sides of the triangle.

Example

In Triangle ABC, ∠A is the included angle formed by consecutive sides AB and AC.

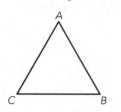

included side

An included side is the side between the two given angles of the triangle.

Example

In Triangle ABC, side AB is the included side formed by consecutive angles A and B.

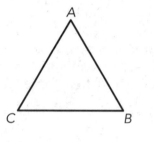

income tax

Income tax is a percentage of a person's or company's earnings that is collected by the government.

Example

If a person earns $90,000 in one year and has to pay an income tax rate of 28%, then that person owes 90,000 × 0.28 or $25,200 in income tax to the government.

inequality

An inequality is any mathematical sentence that has an inequality symbol.

Examples

$8 > 2 \qquad a \leq b \qquad 6.051 > 6.009 \qquad 2x + 4 \geq 16$

inverse operations

Inverse operations are pairs of operations that reverse the effects of each other.

Examples

Addition and subtraction are inverse operations: $351 + 25 - 25 = 351$.

Multiplication and division are inverse operations: $351 \times 25 \div 25 = 351$.

isolate the variable

When you isolate the variable in an equation, you perform an operation, or operations, to get the variable by itself on one side of the equals sign.

Example

In the equation $\frac{a}{b} = \frac{c}{d}$, you can multiply both sides by b to isolate the variable a.

$$b \cdot \frac{a}{b} = b \cdot \frac{c}{d} \longrightarrow a = \frac{bc}{d}$$

—————— L ——————

like terms

In an algebraic expression, like terms are two or more terms that have the same variable raised to the same power.

Examples

like terms

$$4x + 3p + x + 2 = 5x + 3p + 2$$

like terms

$$24a^2 + 2a - 9a^2 = 13a^2 + 2a$$

no like terms

$$m + m^2 - x = x^3$$

line

A line is a straight continuous arrangement of an infinite number of points. A line has an infinite length, but no width. Arrowheads are used to indicate that a line extends infinitely in opposite directions.

Example

Line *AB* is shown.

line segment

A line segment is a portion of a line that includes two points and all the points between those two points.

Example

Line segment *AB* is shown.

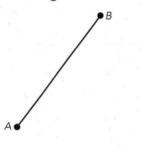

linear expression

A linear expression is any expression in which each term is either a constant or the product of a constant and a single variable raised to the first power.

Examples

$$\frac{1}{2}x + 2, \quad -3 + 12.5x, \quad -1 + 3x + \frac{5}{2}x - \frac{4}{3}$$

linear pair

A linear pair of angles is formed by two adjacent angles that have noncommon sides that form a line.

Examples

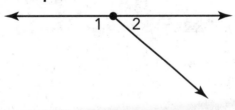

Angles 1 and 2 form a linear pair.

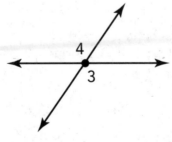

Angles 3 and 4 do NOT form a linear pair.

literal equation

A literal equation is an equation in which the variables represent specific measures.

Examples

$A = lw$ $A = \frac{1}{2}bh$ $d = rt$

M
---

markdown

When businesses sell an item at a lower price than the original price, it is called a markdown.

---

markup

To make money, businesses often buy products from a wholesaler or distributor for one amount and add to that amount to determine the price they use to sell the product to their customers. This is called a markup.

---

means

In a proportion that is written $a : b = c : d$, the two values in the middle, b and c, are the means.

Example

7 books : 14 days = 3 books : 6 days

means

N
---

non-repeating decimals

A non-repeating decimal continues without terminating and without repeating a sequence of digits. Non-repeating decimals are not rational numbers.

Examples

$\sqrt{3} = 1.73205080757\ldots$ $\pi = 3.14159265359\ldots$

non-terminating decimal

A non-terminating decimal is a decimal that continues on infinitely without ending in a sequence of zeros.

Examples

0.333...   1.7272...   3.14159...

---

non-uniform probability model

A non-uniform probability model occurs when all the probabilities in a probability model are not equal to each other.

Example

Outcome	Red	Green	Blue
Probability	$\frac{1}{8}$	$\frac{1}{2}$	$\frac{3}{8}$

O

Order of Operations

The Order of Operations is a set of rules that ensures the same result every time an expression is evaluated.

Example

$44 + (6 - 5) - 2 \times 75 \div 5^1$ Parentheses

$\downarrow$

$44 + 1 - 2 \times 75 \div 5^1$ Exponents

$\downarrow$

$44 + 1 - 2 \times 75 \div 5$ Multiplication and Division (from left to right)

$\downarrow$

$44 + 1 - 150 \div 5$

$\downarrow$

$44 + 1 - 30$ addition and subtraction (from left to right)

$\downarrow$

$45 - 30$

$\downarrow$

15

origin

The origin is a point on a graph with the ordered pair (0, 0).

Example

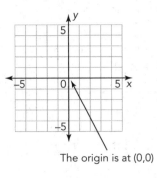

The origin is at (0,0)

outcome

An outcome is the result of a single trial of a probability experiment.

Example

The numbers on the faces of a six-sided number cube are the outcomes that can occur when rolling a six-sided number cube.

——————————— P ———————————

parameter

When data are gathered from a population, the characteristic used to describe the population is called a parameter.

Example

If you wanted to determine the average height of the students at your school, and you measured every student at the school, the characteristic "average height" would be a parameter.

percent decrease

A percent decrease occurs when the new amount is less than the original amount. It is a ratio of the amount of decrease to the original amount.

Example

The price of a $12 shirt has decreased to $8.

$$\frac{12 - 8}{12} = \frac{4}{12} = 0.3 = 33.3\%$$

The percent decrease is 33.3%

percent equation

A percent equation can be written in the form percent × whole = part, where the percent is often written as a decimal.

Example

$$40\% \text{ of } 25 = 10$$

$$(0.40)\ (25) = 10$$

Percent   Part

Whole

percent error (estimation)

Calculating percent error is one way to compare an estimated value to an actual value. To compute percent error, determine the difference between the estimated and actual values and then divide by the actual value.

Example

An airline estimates that they will need an airplane that sits 320 passengers for a flight. An actual 300 tickets were booked for the flight.

$$\text{Percent Error} = \frac{300 - 320}{300} = \frac{-20}{300} \approx -6.7\%$$

percent error (probability)

In probability, the percent error describes how far off the experimental probability is from the theoretical probability as a percent ratio.

Example

Suppose there is one red, one blue, one green, and one yellow marble in a jar. You draw the blue marble 20 times out of 50 trials.

The experimental probability, P_E(blue), is $\frac{20}{50}$ or $\frac{2}{5}$. The theoretical probability, P_T(blue), is $\frac{1}{4}$.

The percent error is $\dfrac{\frac{2}{5} - \frac{1}{4}}{\frac{1}{4}} = \dfrac{\frac{3}{20}}{\frac{1}{4}} = \frac{3}{5}$

$$= 0.6 = 60\%$$

percent increase

A percent increase occurs when the new amount is greater than the original amount. It is a ratio of the amount of increase to the original amount.

Example

The price of a $12 shirt has increased to $13.20.

$$\frac{13.20 - 12}{12} = \frac{1.20}{12} = 0.1 = 10\%$$

The percent increase is 10%.

perpendicular

Two lines, line segments, or rays are perpendicular if they intersect to form 90° angles. The symbol for perpendicular is ⊥.

Example

Line AB is perpendicular to line MN

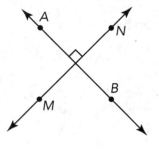

pi

The number pi (π) is the ratio of the circumference of a circle to its diameter. That is $\pi = \frac{C}{d}$, where C is the circumference of the circle, and d is the diameter of the circle.

plane

A plane is a flat surface. It has infinite length and width, but no depth. A plane extends infinitely in all directions in two dimensions. Planes are determined by three points, but are usually named using one uppercase letter.

Example

Plane Q is shown.

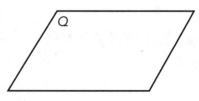

point

A point is a location in space. A point has no size or shape, but it is often represented by using a dot and is named by a capital letter.

Examples

Points A and B are shown.

A •

     • B

population

A population is an entire set of items from which data are collected.

Example

If you wanted to determine the average height of the students at your school, the number of students at the school would be the population.

probability

Probability is the measure of the likelihood that an event will occur. It is a way of assigning a numerical value to the chance that an event will occur by dividing the number of times an event can occur by the number of possible outcomes.

Example

When rolling a six-sided number cube with the numbers 1 through 6 on each face, the probability of rolling a 5, or P(5), is $\frac{1}{6}$.

probability model

A probability model is a list of each possible outcome along with its probability, often shown in a table.

Example

Outcome	1	2	3	4	5	6
Probability	$\frac{1}{6}$	$\frac{1}{6}$	$\frac{1}{6}$	$\frac{1}{6}$	$\frac{1}{6}$	$\frac{1}{6}$

This is a probability model for rolling a six-sided number cube with the numbers 1 through 6 on each face.

Properties of Inequalities

The Properties of Inequalities allow you to solve inequalities involving any numbers.

Examples

- Addition Property of Inequalities
  If $a < b$, then $a + c < b + c$.
  If $a > b$, then $a + c > b + c$.
- Subtraction Property of Inequalities
  If $a < b$, then $a - c < b - c$.
  If $a > b$, then $a - c > b - c$.
- Multiplication Property of Inequalities
  If $a < b$, then $a \cdot c < b \cdot c$, for $c > 0$.
  If $a > b$, then $a \cdot c > b \cdot c$, for $c > 0$.

  If $a < b$, then $a \cdot c > b \cdot c$, for $c < 0$.
  If $a > b$, then $a \cdot c < b \cdot c$, for $c < 0$.
- Division Property of Inequalities
  If $a < b$, then $\frac{a}{c} < \frac{b}{c}$, for $c > 0$.
  If $a > b$, then $\frac{a}{c} > \frac{b}{c}$, for $c > 0$.
  If $a < b$, then $\frac{a}{c} > \frac{b}{c}$, for $c < 0$.
  If $a > b$, then $\frac{a}{c} < \frac{b}{c}$, for $c < 0$.

proportion

A proportion is an equation that states that two ratios are equal.

Example

$\frac{1}{2} = \frac{4.5}{9}$

proportional relationship

A proportional relationship is one in which the ratio of the inputs to the outputs is constant. For a relationship to illustrate a proportional relationship, all the ratios $\frac{y}{x}$ or $\frac{x}{y}$, must represent the same constant.

radius

The radius of a circle is a line segment formed by connecting a point on the circle and the center of the circle.

Example

In the circle, O is the center and segment OA is the radius.

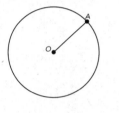

random number table

A random number table is a table that displays random digits. These tables can contain hundreds of digits.

Example

| Line 7 | 54621 | 62117 | 55516 | 40467 |

random sample

A random sample is a sample that is selected from the population in such a way that every member of the population has the same chance of being selected.

Example

If you wanted to determine the average height of the students at your school, you could choose just a certain number of students randomly and measure their heights. This group of students would be a random sample.

ray

A ray is a part of a line that begins at a point and extends infinitely in one direction. Rays are named using two points. The first point represents the starting point, and the second point can be any other point on the ray.

Example

Ray AB is shown.

regular polygon

A regular polygon is a polygon with all sides congruent and all angles congruent.

Examples

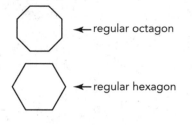

regular octagon

regular hexagon

repeating decimal

A repeating decimal is a decimal in which a digit, or a group of digits, repeat(s) infinitely. Repeating decimals are rational numbers.

Examples

$\frac{1}{9} = 0.111...$ $\frac{7}{12} = 0.58333...$

$\frac{22}{7} = 3.142857142857...$

—————————— S ——————————

sales tax

Sales tax is a percentage of the selling price of a good or service which is added to the price.

Example

You want to purchase an item for $8.00 in a state where the sales tax is 6.25%, therefore you will pay 8×0.0625 or $0.50 in sales tax. You will pay a total of $8.50 for the item.

sample

A sample is a selection from a population.

Example

If you wanted to determine the average height of the students in your school, you could choose a certain number of students and measure their heights. The heights of the students in this group would be your sample.

sample space

A list of all possible outcomes of an experiment is called a sample space.

Example

When rolling a six-sided number cube that has one number, from 1 through 6, on each face, the sample space is {1, 2, 3, 4, 5, 6}.

scale

A scale is a ratio that compares two measures.

Example

1 cm : 4 cm

scale drawing

A scale drawing is a representation of a real object or place that is in proportion to the real object or place it represents.

Examples

A map or a blueprint is an example of a scale drawing.

scale factor

When you multiply a measure by a scale to produce a reduced or enlarged measure, the scale is called a scale factor.

Example

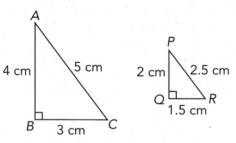

The scale factor from Triangle ABC to Triangle PQR is $\frac{1}{2}$.

sides of an angle

The sides of an angle are the two rays that make up the angle.

Example

The sides of Angle CAB are made up of Ray AB and Ray AC.

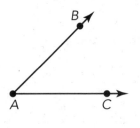

similar figures

Figures that are proportional in size, or that have proportional dimensions, are called similar figures.

Example

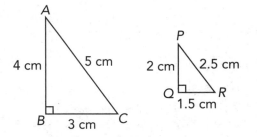

Triangle ABC and Triangle PQR are similar figures.

simple event

A simple event is an event consisting of one outcome.

Example

When rolling a six-sided number cube with the numbers 1 through 6 on each face, rolling a 5 is a simple event.

simple interest

Simple interest is a type of interest that is a fixed percent of the principal. Simple interest is paid over a specific period of time—either twice a year or once a year, for example. The formula for simple interest is $I = P \times r \times t$, where I represents the interest earned, P represents the amount of the principal, r represents the interest rate, and t represents the time that the money earns interest.

Example

Kim deposits $300 into a savings account at a simple interest rate of 5% per year. The formula can be used to calculate the simple interest Kim will have earned at the end of 3 years.

Interest = Principal × rate × time

Interest = (300)(0.05)(3)

$\qquad$ = $45

simulation

A simulation is an experiment that models a real-life situation.

sketch

A sketch is a freehand drawing of an object.

solution set

The solution set is the set of all values of the variable that make an inequality or equation true.

Examples

$x \geq 7$

The solution set for $x \geq 7$ is all the numbers greater than or equal to 7.

$|x| = 3$

The solution set for $|x| = 3$ is {−3, 3}.

solve a proportion

To solve a proportion means to determine all the values of the variables that make the proportion true.

solve an inequality

To solve an inequality means to determine the values of the variable that make the inequality true.

Example

$2x + 4 \geq 16$

$\quad 2x \geq 12$

$\quad\quad x \geq 6$

Any value for x that is greater than or equal to 6 will make the inequality true.

statistic

When data are gathered from a sample, the characteristic used to describe the sample is called a statistic.

Example

If you wanted to determine the average height of the students in your school, and you chose just a certain number of students randomly and measured their heights, the characteristic "average height" would be called a statistic.

straight angle

A straight angle is formed when the sides of the angle point in exactly opposite directions. The two legs form a straight line through the vertex.

Example

Angle *CAB* is a straight angle.

straightedge

A straightedge is a ruler with no numbers.

supplementary angles

Two angles are supplementary angles if the sum of their angle measures is equal to 180°.

Example

Angles 1 and 2 are supplementary angles.

survey

A survey is one method of collecting data in which people are asked one or more questions.

Example

A restaurant may ask its customers to complete a survey with the following question:

On a scale of 1–10, with 1 meaning "poor" and 10 meaning "excellent," how would you rate the food you ate?

——— T ———

terminating decimal

A terminating decimal has a finite number of digits, meaning that after a finite number of decimal places, all following decimal places have a value of 0. Terminating decimals are rational numbers.

Examples

$\dfrac{9}{10} = 0.9 \qquad \dfrac{15}{8} = 1.875 \qquad \dfrac{193}{16} = 12.0625$

theoretical probability

The theoretical probability of an event is the ratio of the number of desired outcomes to the total possible outcomes.

Example

Suppose there is one red, one blue, one green, and one yellow marble in a jar. The theoretical probability of drawing a blue marble, P_T(blue), is $\dfrac{1}{4}$.

tree diagram

A tree diagram illustrates the possible outcomes of a given situation. It has two main parts: the branches and the ends. An outcome of each event is written at the end of each branch.

Example

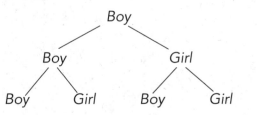

Triangle Inequality Theorem

The Triangle Inequality Theorem states that the sum of the lengths of any two sides of a triangle is greater than the length of the third side.

two-step equation

A two-step equation requires that two inverse operations be performed in order to isolate the variable.

U
---

uniform probability model

A uniform probability model occurs when all the probabilities in a probability model are equally likely to occur.

Example

Outcome	1	2	3	4	5	6
Probability	$\frac{1}{6}$	$\frac{1}{6}$	$\frac{1}{6}$	$\frac{1}{6}$	$\frac{1}{6}$	$\frac{1}{6}$

unit rate

A unit rate is a comparison of two different measurements in which the numerator or denominator has a value of one unit.

Example

The speed 60 miles in 2 hours can be written as a unit rate:

$$\frac{60 \text{ mi}}{2 \text{ h}} = \frac{30 \text{ mi}}{1 \text{ h}}.$$

The unit rate is 30 miles per hour.

---

unit rate of change

The unit rate of change describes the amount the dependent variable changes for every unit the independent variable changes.

V
---

variable

A variable is a letter or symbol that is used to represent a number.

Examples

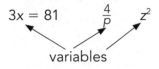

variables

vertex

A vertex of an angle is the common endpoint the two rays that make up the sides of the angle share.

Example

The vertex of $\angle CAB$ is point A.

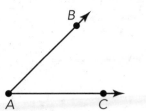

vertical angles

Vertical angles are two nonadjacent angles that are formed by two intersecting lines.

Examples

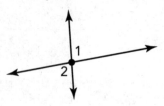

Angles 1 and 2 are vertical angles.

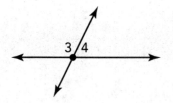

Angles 3 and 4 are NOT vertical angles.

zero pair

A positive counter and a negative counter together make a zero pair, since the total value of the pair is zero.

Example

$\oplus + \ominus = 0$

Index

Symbols
: (colon), M1-75
<, >, ≤, ≥, = (inequality symbols), M3-97
↔ (line symbol), M5-9
⊥ (perpendicular symbol), M5-25
π (pi), M2-106, M1-12–M1-13, M1-24

A
Absolute value
  in adding integers, M2-20–M2-21, M2-22, M2-24, M2-40
  definition of, M2-20
  in subtracting integers, M2-27, M2-65
Adding integers, M2-17–M2-48
  absolute value in, M2-20–M2-21, M2-22, M2-24, M2-40
  additive inverses, M2-33–M2-34, M2-42–M2-44
  on a number line, M2-18–M2-30, M2-43
  patterns in, M2-32
  rule for, M2-41–M2-42, M2-45
  using two-color counters, M2-35–M2-39, M2-43
  zeros in, M2-32
Adding rational numbers, M2-69–M2-73, M2-76–M2-78
Addition equations, solving, M-58–M-59
Addition Property of Equality, M3-73
Additive inverses, M2-33–M2-34, M2-42–M2-44
  definition of, M2-33

Adjacent angles, M5-27–M5-28
Algebraic expressions
  constraint (See Constraint in algebraic expression)
  definition of, M3-9
  evaluating (See Evaluate an algebraic expression)
  factoring, M3-27–M3-29
  linear expression (See Linear expressions)
  on number line, M3-21–M3-22
  solving addition equation, M3-58–M3-59
  solving subtraction equation, M3-60
  substitution with rational numbers, M3-11–M3-12
Angles
  adjacent, M5-27–M5-28
  complementary, M5-22–M5-24
  definition of, M5-14
  duplicate, M5-22
  linear pairs, M5-29–M5-32
  perpendicular lines, M5-25–M5-26
  perpendicular relationships, M5-25
  right, M5-25
  sides of, M5-14–M5-15
  straight, M5-20
  supplementary, M5-22–M5-24
  vertex of, M5-14
  vertical, M5-32–M5-34
Arc
  definition of, M5-11
Area of a circle

composite figure problems, M1-36
  formula for, M1-21–M1-23
  maximum area problem, M1-35
  shaded region problems, M1-37–M1-40
  strategy to determine, M1-34
Associative property, M2-126

B
Bar notation, M2-106
Base of a pyramid, M5-98
Blueprint, scale drawings, M1-235–M1-236
Box-and-whisker plot
  comparing two populations with, M4-189, M4-192

C
Center of a circle, M1-10
Circles
  arc, M5-11
  area of, M1-19–M1-32
  center of, M1-10
  circumference of (See Circumference of a circle)
  definition of, M1-8, M1-10
  diameter of (See Diameter of a circle)
  naming, M1-9–M1-10
  parts of, M1-9–M1-10
  radius, M1-10
  radius of (See Radius of a circle)
Circumference formula
  vs. area formula, M1-24–M1-25
  diameter in, M1-12
  pi in, M1-12–M1-13

Circumference of a circle,
M1-7–M1-18
vs. area of a circle,
M1-24–M1-25
definition of, M1-6, M1-17
measuring, M1-11, M1-15
See also Circumference
formula
Combining like terms
with decimal and fractional
coefficients,
M3-38–M3-39
definition of, M3-35
in evaluating an algebraic
expression, M3-37
in linear expressions,
M3-35–M3-37
Commission,
M1-188–M1-191
Common factor
definition of, M3-27
greatest (GCF),
M3-27–M3-29
Commutative property,
M2-126
Compass, M5-8
Complementary angles,
M5-22–M5-24
Complementary events,
M4-12–M4-13
Complex ratio, M1-60
Composite figures,
M5-117–M5-125
Compound events
definition of, M4-105
probability of,
M4-113–M4-124
determining with "and"
or "or," M4-105–M4-
106, M4-109
randomly choice,
M4-107–M4-109
Compound probabilities,
M4-113–M4-121
Congruent, M5-11
Congruent angles,
M5-23
Constant of proportionality
definition of, M1-112
determining,
M1-109–M1-125
in graphs, M1-127–M1-138
meaning of,
M1-114–M1-117

problems solved with,
M1-120–M1-121
proportional relationships
with equations,
M1-118–M1-120
proportions solved with,
M1-120–M1-121
Constant of variation.
See Constant of
proportionality
Constant term,
M3-137–M3-138
Constraint in algebraic
expression, M3-9
Construct, M5-8
See also Geometric
constructions
Converting temperatures,
M3-174
Corresponding angles,
M1-224
Corresponding sides, M1-224
Cross-sections
of a cube, M5-76–M5-73
definition of, M5-77
of a right rectangular prism,
M5-91, M5-93
of a right rectangular
pyramid,
M5-97–M5-106
of a square, M5-77–M5-78,
M5-80, M5-82, M5-84
Cubes, cross-sections of,
M5-77–M5-81
vs. cross-sections of a right
rectangular prism,
M5-86
description of, M5-79,
M5-87, M5-89
diagram of, M5-79, M5-87,
M5-89
names of, M5-79,
M5-80–M5-81, M5-89

D

Data
analyzing, M4-176–M4-177
(*See also* Five number
summary)
definition of, M4-134,
M4-205
distribution of (*See*
Distribution of data)
sample as, M4-136

Data collection
five number summary,
M4-176–M4-177
formulating questions,
M4-144
through random sampling,
M4-151–M4-164
Decimals
classifying,
M2-105–M2-106
Diameter of a circle
in circumference formula,
M1-12
vs. circumference of a
circle, M1-11
definition of, M1-10
Direct proportions
constant of proportionality
in, M1-141–M1-148
example of, M1-102
Direct variation
definition of, M1-101,
M1-154
determining how quantities
vary directly,
M1-101–M1-102
percent equation and,
M1-172–M1-173
tips and, M1-184–M1-185
Discounts, M3-38, M3-47
Distribution of data
in comparing two
populations, M4-172,
M4-175–M4-177
dot plot used in,
M4-155–M4-156,
M4-158–M4-159,
M4-161, 755
mean determined by,
M4-154
median determined by,
M4-154
skewed left, M4-154
skewed right,
M4-154
symmetric, M4-154
Distributive properties
algebraic expressions
factored by using,
M3-27–M3-29
algebraic expressions
simplified by using,
M2-129

applying in algebraic
equations,
M3-23–M3-26
Distributive Property of
adding the opposite to
subtract, M3-40–M3-41
Dividing by negative
numbers,
M3-105–M3-108
Dividing by positive numbers,
M3-101–M3-104
Division as inverse operation,
M1-78
Division Property of Equality,
M3-78, M3-80
Dot plot
comparing two populations
on, M4-172, M4-173,
M4-178, M4-184
in distribution of data,
M4-155–M4-156,
M4-158–M4-159
in random sample,
M4-155–M4-156,
M4-158–M4-159

E
Efficiency, solving equations
with, M3-84–M3-87
Endpoints, M5-10
Equal expressions
creating a model to
represent, M3-55
modelling equations as,
M3-53–M3-54
Equality
properties of, M3-78,
M3-80
with proportion,
M1-71–M1-73
Equally likely, M4-19
Equations
definition of, M3-52
fractions in, solving, M3-85
interpreting forms of,
M3-148–M3-149
interpreting situations
with more than one
quadrant,
M3-130–M3-134
inverse operations to solve,
M3-77–M3-78
model creation to solve an,
M3-56–M3-57

picture algebra used in,
M3-53–M3-54
same, different forms,
M3-141–M3-143
solving (See Solve an
equation)
two-step (See Two-step
equations)
using
to create table,
M1-142–M1-143
graph to write an, M1-141
scenario to write an,
M1-145–M1-146
writing, with signed
numbers, M2-10–M2-16
See also Negative solutions
to problem situations
Equilateral triangles, M1-245
Equivalent rational numbers,
M2-107–M2-109
in fractional form,
M2-108–M2-109
Evaluate an algebraic
expression, M3-7–M3-8
combining like terms and,
M3-36, M3-37
definition of, M3-13
Events
complementary,
M4-12–M4-13
definition of, M4-9
probability of, determining,
M4-9–M4-18
simple, M4-9
Experiment
definition of, M4-9
greatest and least possible
probability in,
M4-17–M4-18
sample space for, M4-9,
M4-14, M4-19
simulating, M4-47–M4-64
See also Trials
Experimental probability,
M4-37–M4-39
calculating, M4-39
definition of, M4-36
formula for, M4-36
probability models for,
M4-25
in simulation trials,
M4-49–M4-51
of sums, M4-76–M4-77

vs. theoretical probability,
M4-42
Extremes
definition of, M1-76
multiplying, M1-76
proportions solved with,
M1-76–M1-78
variables isolated by
multiplying, M1-78

F
Fractional rates, solving
problems with,
M1-65–M1-66,
M1-69–M1-82
Factoring
algebraic expressions,
M3-27–M3-29
linear expressions,
M3-27–M3-30
definition of, M2-128
Fees and graphs, M1-205
Five number summary,
M4-176–M4-180
box-and-whisker plot used
to display, M4-189,
M4-192
comparing two populations
with, M4-176, M4-188

G
Geometric constructions
Euclid and construction,
M5-8
line segments, duplicate,
M5-12–M5-13
See also Angles
Geometry
building blocks of,
M5-9–M5-11
noice-canceling, M5-130
See also Geometric
constructions
Graphs
axis of, labelling,
M1-102
constant of proportionality
in, M1-127–M1-138
in direct variation,
M1-101–M1-105
fees and, M1-205
inequalities representations
on, M3-160–M3-161

interpreting situations
with more than one
quadrant,
M3-130–M3-134
of linear equations,
comparing,
M3-144–M3-147
in multiple representations,
solving problems with,
M3-174, M3-176,
M3-177
proportional relationship of,
M1-134–M1-138
proportionality from,
M1-103–M1-105
to write an equation,
M1-141
of two constants of
proportionality,
M1-130–M1-131
Graphing
equations and inequalities,
M3-162–M3-164
linear equations,
M3-127–M3-129
Greatest common factor
(GCF), M3-27–M3-29
Grids, M1-229

H
Histogram
comparing two populations
on, M4-190

I
Included angle, M5-59
Included side, M5-60
Income tax,
M1-203–M1-204
Inequalities
adding and subtracting
with, M3-97–M3-100
equations versus, M3-96
on graphs, M3-160–M3-
161, M3-167–M3-168
graphing equations and,
M3-162–M3-166
with inverse operations,
M3-95–M3-116
solving two-step,
M3-105–M3-108
Inequality symbols ($<$, $>$, $\leq$,
$\geq$, $=$), M3-97

Inferences, random
samples to draw,
M4-151–M4-167
Integers
adding (See Adding
integers)
dividing, M2-98–M2-99
models used to understand
integer addition,
M2-7–M2-9
multiplication of,
M2-89–M2-94
negative, M2-7–M2-13
positive, M2-7–M2-13
quotients of,
M2-103–M2-112
signed multiplication facts,
M2-95–M2-100
subtracting (See
Subtracting integers)
writing number sentences,
M2-43
Interquartile Range (IQR)
in comparing two
populations, M4-176,
M4-188
definition of, M4-170
Intersection, M4-102
Inverse operations
definition of, M1-78
in solving equations,
M3-77–M3-78
strategies for applying,
M3-79–M3-81
in two-step equations,
M3-79
Isolating variables, M1-78
Isosceles triangles, M5-65

L
Like terms
combining with decimal
and fractional
coefficients,
M3-38–M3-39
combining in linear
expressions,
M3-35–M3-37
definition of, M3-35
Linear equations
comparing graphs of,
M3-144–M3-147
graphing, M3-127–M3-129

structure of,
M3-139–M3-140
Linear expressions
combining like terms in,
M3-35–M3-37
definition of, M3-9
factoring, M3-27–M3-30
Linear pairs, M5-29–M5-32
Lines
description of, M5-9
perpendicular, M5-25
in perpendicular
relationships, M5-25
ray, M5-14
symbol for ($\leftrightarrow$), M5-9
Line segments
definition of, M5-10
duplicate, M5-12–M5-13
endpoints of, M5-10
Literal equations
definition of, M3-87
solving, M3-87–M3-89

M
Maps, scale drawings of,
M1-233–M1-234
Markdown, definition of,
M1-166
Markup, definition of,
M1-166
Mean absolute deviation
calculating, M4-173,
M4-192
vs. calculating the
measures of center,
M4-185
in comparing two
populations, M4-173,
M4-192
definition of, M4-170
Means
in comparing two
populations,
M4-172–M4-173,
M4-184
congruent, M1-49,
M5-11
definition of, M1-76
vs. median, M4-154
proportions solved with,
M1-76–M1-78
in random sampling,
M4-154

variables isolated by multiplying, M1-78

Measures of center
comparing two populations to, M4-169–M4-193
comparing variation and, M4-171–M4-174
mean *vs.* median in, M4-154

Measures of variation
comparing two populations to, M4-169–M4-180
drawing conclusions about two populations from, M4-184, M4-188–M4-189, M4-193
for random samples from two populations, M4-181–M4-193

Measures of variability
comparing two populations to, M4-169–M4-193

Median
in comparing two populations, M4-176
in five number summary, M4-176, M4-177
vs. mean, M4-154

Multiple representations, solving problems with, M3-169–M3-180
equations used in, M3-174
graphs used in, M3-173, M3-175, M3-177
proportional relationships, M1-147–M1-150
tables used in, M3-173, M3-175, M3-176, M3-177
See also Two-step equations

Multiplication
of extremes, M1-76
of integers, M2-91–M2-94
as inverse operation, M1-78
of means, M1-76
patterns in, M2-95–M2-96, M2-98
of proportions to isolate the variable, M1-78
rule for, M2-96

signed fact families, M2-95–M2-100

Multiplication Property of Equality, M3-78

Multiplying by negative numbers, M3-105–M3-108

Multiplying by positive numbers, M3-101–M3-104

Negative numbers
multiplying and dividing by, M3-105–M3-108

Non-repeating decimals
analyzing, M2-106
definition of, M2-106
π as, M2-106

Non-terminating decimals
analyzing, M2-105–M2-106
defined, M2-105

Non-uniform probability model, M4-26, M4-30, M4-103

Number line
algebraic expressions on, M3-21–M3-22
integers added on, M2-18–M2-30, M2-43
integers subtracted on, M2-51–M2-54
for solving inequalities, M3-65–M3-75

Number sentences, M2-28, M2-43

Numerator
in scaling down, M1-69
in scaling up, M1-69

Numeric expressions
distributing and factoring with -1, M2-127–M2-128
practicing with number properties, M2-130–M2-132
with signed numbers, M2-125–M2-126

O

Origin, M1-92

Outcomes
definition of, M4-9
determining, M4-14–M4-16

proportional reasoning to predict, M4-40
sum of the probabilities for all, M4-20
tree diagrams used to determine, M4-92–M4-98M4-107

P

Parallelograms, cross-sections of, M5-78, M5-81, M5-82, M5-85

Parameter, M4-136, M4-153

Pasta triangle, M5-43–M5-45

Percent decreases, M1-212–M1-214

Percent equations
definition of, M1-179
direct variations and, M1-172–M1-173
forms of, writing, M1-179–M1-181
introduction to, M1-179–M1-181
involving proportions, using, M1-181–M1-182

Percent error
calculating, M2-118–M2-119
defined, M2-118, M4-42, M4-160
experimental probability and, M4-42–M4-43
formula for, M4-42

Percent increases, M1-211

Percent models, M1-163–M1-164

Percent problems
appreciation, M1-215
commission, M1-188–M1-191
depreciation, M1-215–M1-216
increase and decrease with geometry, M1-217–M1-218
percent models used in, M1-163–M1-164
principal, M1-186–M1-187
proportions in, M1-165–M1-168, M1-174–M1-176

simple interest,
M1-186–M1-187
solving, M1-161–M1-176
tips, M1-180–M1-181,
M1-184–M1-185
Percents
calculating,
M1-181–M1-182
decreases in,
M1-212–M1-214
equations (*See* Percent
equations)
error (*See* Percent error)
probabilities expressed as,
M4-17–M4-18
problems (*See* Percent
problems)
Perpendicular, M5-25
Perpendicular lines,
M5-25–M5-26
Perpendicular relationships,
M5-25
Perpendicular symbol (⊥),
M5-25
Picture algebra, M3-53–M3-
63
Pi (π)
in area formula, M1-24
in circumference formula,
M1-12–M1-13
as non-repeating decimals,
M2-106
Plane, description of, M5-9
Pocket probabilities, M4-24
Point, description of, M5-9
Polygons
areas of regular,
M5-147–M5-149
Population
accurate characteristics of,
M4-138
comparing two (*See*
Populations, comparing
two)
definition of, M4-135
parameters of, M4-136,
M4-153
vs. sample, M4-137
Populations, comparing two
on box-and-whisker plot,
M4-189, M4-192
distribution of data,
M4-172, M4-175

on dot plot, M4-172,
M4-173, M4-178,
M4-184
five number summary used
in, M4-176, M4-188
on histogram, M4-190
mean absolute deviation in,
M4-173, M4-192
means in, M4-172–M4-173,
M4-184
to measures of center,
M4-169–M4-193
measures of spread,
determining, M4-178
to measures of variability,
M4-169–M4-193
on stem-and-leaf plots,
M4-175
Positive numbers
multiplying and dividing by,
M3-101–M3-104
Predictions
for experimental
probability, M4-39
number lines to, using,
M3-96
of outcomes, proportional
reasoning used for,
M4-40
samples to justify,
M4-161–M4-162
sample space for, M4-35,
M4-37
Principal, M1-187
Probability
of compound events,
M4-113–M4-124
definition of, M4-9
determining,
M4-9–M4-11
equally likely, M4-19
of an event, determining,
M4-9–M4-18
experimental (*See*
Experimental
probability)
expressed as fractions,
decimals, or percents,
M4-17–M4-18
introduction to,
M4-6–M4-46
models (*See* Probability
models)

predicting, M4-16, M4-35,
M4-37–M4-39
of products, M4-82–M4-84
sum of, for all outcomes,
M4-20
theoretical (*See* Theoretical
probability)
tree diagrams used to
determine,
M4-92–M4-98, M4-107
See also Outcomes
Probability models,
M4-23–M4-32
to calculate compound
probabilities,
M4-101–M4-112
constructing,
M4-27–M4-28,
M4-94–M4-98
definition of, M4-25
for experimental
probability, M4-25,
M4-91
interpreting, M4-27–M4-28
non-uniform, M4-26,
M4-103
outcomes listed in,
M4-25–M4-26
for random selection,
M4-29
sum of, M4-24, M4-25
in tables, M4-25, M4-29
for theoretical probability
M4-90–M4-91, M4-96
tree diagrams,
M4-92–M4-98,
M4-107
uniform, M4-26, M4-103
using, M4-94–M4-98
Products, probabilities of,
M4-82–M4-84
Properties of Equality, M3-73
Proportionality constants.
See Constant of
proportionality
Proportionality
commissions and,
M1-188–M1-191
from tables and graphs,
M1-103–M1-105
Proportional reasoning to
predict outcomes,
M4-40

Proportional relationships,
 M1-91–M1-108
 definition of, M1-95–M1-96
 multiple representations of,
  M1-147–M1-150
 situational problems and,
  M1-97–M1-101
 using equations, M1-142,
  M1-150
 using graphs, M1-141,
  M1-150
 using scenarios,
  M1-144–M1-146,
  M1-150
 using tables, M1-142–M1-
  143, M1-150
Proportions
 constant of proportionality
  used to solve,
  M1-120–M1-121
 definition of, M1-70
 equality with,
  M1-71–M1-73
 solving
  with means and extremes,
   M1-73–M1-78
 problems with,
  M1-79–M1-80
 to solve percent problems,
  M1-161–M1-176
Protractor, M5-8, M5-20,
 M5-21
Pyramids
 base of, M5-98, M5-141
 definition of, M5-98
 naming, M5-144
 right rectangular,
  M5-97–M5-103
 slant height of a regular,
  M5-131
 surface area of,
  M5-131–M5-138
 vertex of, M5-105
 volume of, M5-112–M5-113

Q

Quotient of integers,
 M2-103–M2-106

R

Radius of a circle, M1-10,
 M1-13
 in area formula for a circle,
  M1-24

in circumference formula,
 M1-13
 definition of, M1-10
 radii as plural of, M1-10
Random number generator,
 M4-142
Random number tables
 example of, M4-202
 random sample chosen
  from, M4-158
 to select a sample,
  M4-142–M4-146
Random sample
 comparing,
  M4-186–M4-189
 definition of, M4-138
 distributions of data in,
  M4-151–M4-156
 dot plot used in,
  M4-155–M4-156,
  M4-158–M4-159
 to draw inferences,
  M4-151–M4-167
 to make predictions,
  M4-157–M4-160
 random number tables
  used to choose, M4-158
 selecting, M4-139–M4-141
 selecting squares randomly,
  M4-152
 simulating,
  M4-183–M4-185
Rate of change. See Unit rate
 of change
Rates
 fractional, M1-51–M1-86
 See also Unit rate
Ratio
 of circle, exploring,
  M1-7–M1-18
 constant of proportionality,
  M1-109–M1-125

 Pi as ultimate, M1-7–M1-18
Rational numbers
 adding, M2-69–M2-73,
  M2-76–M2-78
 algebraic expressions
  substitution with,
  M3-11–M3-12
 distance between,
  M2-62–M2-66
 dividing, M2-89–M2-138
 in equations, using, M2-117

equivalent,
 M2-107–M2-109
 evaluating expressions
  with, M2-120–M2-122
 multiplying, M2-89–M2-138
 number properties with,
  using, M2-125–M2-132
 operating with, to solve
  problems,
  M2-115–M2-116
 ratios of fractions
  comparing, M1-61
 simulation using,
  M4-55–M4-61
 subtracting, M2-74–M2-75
 solving problems with,
  M1-65
 unit rates determination
  from, M1-62–M1-64
Ray, M5-14
Regular polygons
 areas of, M5-147–M5-149
 calculation of,
  M5-150–M5-151
 definition of, M5-147
Repeating decimals
 analyzing, M2-106
 bar notation used for,
  M2-106
 definition of, M2-106
 fractions represented as,
  M2-106
Right angles
 forming, M5-25
 in perpendicular
  relationships, M5-25
Right rectangular prisms
 measuring,
  M5-145–M5-147
 naming of, M5-144
 solids with regular bases,
  M5-151–M5-153
 volume of, M5-109–M5-110
Right rectangular prisms,
 cross-sections of,
  M5-75–M5-96
 vs. cross-sections of a cube,
  M5-86
 description of, M5-83,
  M5-93
 diagram of, M5-83, M5-91,
  M5-93
 names of, M5-83,
  M5-84–M5-85

Right rectangular pyramids
  composite figures,
    M5-117–M5-125
  cross-sections of,
    M5-100–M5-102
  descriptions of, M5-103
  diagrams of, M5-103
  measuring,
    M5-145–M5-147
  shapes of, M5-101
Right rectangular pyramids,
    cross-sections of,
    M5-97–M5-106
  vs. cross-sections of a cube,
    M5-86
  description of, M5-98,
    M5-103
  diagram of, M5-101,
    M5-103
  names of, M5-101, M5-103

S

Sales tax, M1-198–M1-202
Sample
  analyzing displays of data
    from, M4-190–M4-193
  comparing random,
    M4-186–M4-189
  definition of, M36
  to justify predictions,
    M4-161–M4-162
  ratio to find total area of,
    M4-153, M4-156
  selecting random,
    M4-139–M4-141
  representative,
    M4-135–M4-138
  statistics, M4-136
  using multiple, to make
    predictions,
    M4-153–M4-156
  See also Random sample;
    Sample space
Sample space
  definition of, M4-9
  for experiments, M4-9,
    M4-14, M4-19
  for predictions, M4-35,
    M4-37
  for probabilities, M4-82
  for simulation, M4-49
  for theoretical probability,
    M4-37

Scale, M1-225
Scale drawings
  creating, M1-229–M1-230
  definition of, M1-227
  interpreting,
    M1-237–M1-238
Scale factor
  definition of, M1-225
  See also Scale drawings
Sides of an angle, M5-14
Signed numbers
  numeric expressions with,
    M2-125–M2-126
  writing equations with,
    M2-10–M2-13
Similar figures,
    M1-231–M1-232
Simple event, M4-9
Simple interest,
    M1-186–M1-187
Simulation
  definition of, M4-49
  to estimate compound
    probabilities,
    M4-113–M4-121
  experimental probability in,
    M4-49–M4-51
  of experiments,
    M4-47–M4-64
  of random numbers,
    M4-55–M4-61,
    M4-183–M4-185
  technology used in,
    M4-142
  theoretical probability in,
    M4-50, M4-53
  trials of, M4-51–M4-54
Sketch, M5-8
Slant height of a pyramid,
    M5-138
Solve an equation
  creating a model to,
    M3-56–M3-57
  on double number line,
    M3-65–M3-67
  with efficiency,
    M3-84–M3-87
  inverse operations used in,
    M3-77–M3-78
  Properties of Equality used
    in, M3-73
  two-step, M3-68–M3-71,
    M3-79

Solve an inequality, M3-97
Solve a proportion
  definition of, M1-76
Solving
  addition equation,
    M3-58–M3-59
  literal equations,
    M3-87–M3-89
  number riddle,
    M3-90–M3-91
  subtraction equation,
    M3-60
Solution set, M3-97
Squares, cross-sections of,
    M5-77–M5-78, M5-80,
    M5-82, M5-84
Squares, selecting,
    M4-152
Square units, M1-245
Statistic, M4-136
Statistical process, reviewing,
    M4-134
Stem-and-leaf plots,
    comparing two
    populations on,
    M4-175
Straight angles, M5-20
Straightedge, M5-8
Subtraction as adding the
    opposite, M2-129,
    M3-40–M3-42
Subtracting integers,
    M2-49–M2-68
  absolute value in, M2-27
  on a number line,
    M2-51–M2-54
  patterns in, M2-60–M2-61
  rules for, M2-65–M2-66
  two-color counters used in,
    M2-55–M2-59
  zero pairs, M2-56
Subtracting rational numbers,
    M2-74–M2-75
Subtraction Property of
    Equality, M3-73
Supplementary angles,
    M5-22–M5-24
Surface area
  formula for, M5-139
  of pyramids,
    M5-131–M5-142
  of square pyramids,
    M5-134

of three-dimensional
 objects,
 M5-129–M5-160
fo triangular pyramid,
 M5-135–M5-136
Survey
 census and,
 M4-135–M4-136
 data in, M4-134
 definition of, M4-134
 results from, example of,
 M4-146
 See also Data collection

T

Tables
 to create a scenario,
 M1-144
 in evaluating an
 algebraic expression,
 M3-14–M3-15
 in multiple representations,
 solving problems with,
 M3-173, M3-175,
 M3-176, M3-177
 in probability models,
 M4-24, M4-25, M4-29
 proportionality from,
 M1-103–M1-105
 proportions on, M1-79,
 M1-92, M1-122
 using an equation to
 create, M1-142–M1-143
 See also Random number
 tables
Taxes, M1-197–M1-208
Temperatures, converting,
 M3-174
Terminating decimals
 analyzing, M2-105
 defined, M2-105
Theoretical probability,
 M4-37–M4-39
 definition of, M4-36
 vs. experimental
 probability,
 M4-40–M4-42
 formula for, M4-36
 probability models for,
 M4-96
 in simulation trials, M4-50,
 M4-53
 of sums, M4-78–M4-81

Three-dimensional figures,
 M5-73–M5-160
 cubes, M5-76–M5-96
 right rectangular prisms,
 M5-75–M5-96
 right rectangular pyramids,
 M5-97–M5-103
 surface area,
 M5-129–M5-156
 volume, M5-107–M5-127
 See also Cross-sections
Tips, M1-184–M1-185
Trapezoids, cross-sections
 of, M5-99, M5-101,
 M5-103
Tree diagrams
 definition of, M4-94
 probabilities determined
 with, M4-94–M4-98,
 M4-96–M4-97, M4-107
Trials
 conducting, M4-36, M4-42
 experimental probability in,
 M4-49–M4-51
 of simulation,
 M4-51–M4-61
 theoretical probability in,
 M4-51, M4-53
Triangle drawings, M1-224
Triangle Inequality Theorem,
 M5-48–M5-49
Triangles
 cross-sections of, M5-78,
 M5-80, M5-83, M5-84,
 M5-101, M5-103
 pasta, M5-43–M5-45
Triangles, constructing
 given included angles or
 included sides,
 M5-59–M5-62
 given three angles,
 M5-55–M5-56
 given three line segments,
 M5-45–M5-47
 given two angles,
 M5-41–M5-42
 given two angles and
 one line segment,
 M5-57–M5-58
 given two line segments,
 M5-41–M5-42
 Triangle Inequality
 Theorem, M5-48–M5-49

Two-step equations
 definition of, M3-79
 inverse operations used in,
 M3-79–M3-81
 simplifying, M3-81–M3-83
 solving, M3-93–M3-94
Two-step inequalities
 solving, M3-109–M3-112,
 M3-115–M3-116

U

Uniform probability model,
 M4-26, M4-103
Unit rate
 best buy determined by,
 M1-27
 definition of, M1-26
 denominator in, M1-26,
 M1-44
 determining, M1-53–M1-58
 from ratios of fractions,
 M1-62–M1-64
 representations,
 M1-51–M1-58
Unit rate of change
 calculating, M3-171, M3-174
 definition of, M3-183
 equations used in,
 M3-174–M3-176
 graphs used in, M3-173,
 M3-175, M3-177
 inequality used to solve,
 M3-158
 in multiple representations
 of equations,
 M3-157–M3-159
 tables used in, M3-157,
 M3-173, M3-175,
 M3-176, M3-177

V

Values
 direct variation in, M1-101
 lines drawn on a graph to
 interpret, M1-100
 See also Absolute value
Variables
 in algebraic expressions,
 M3-8, M3-10, M3-13
 definition of, M3-9
 evaluating rational numbers
 with expressions and,
 M2-120–M2-121

isolating, M1-78
in like terms, M3-36
in proportions, M1-71
See also Inequalities
Vertex
definition of, M5-14
of a pyramid, M5-105
Vertical angles, M5-32–M5-34
Volume
doubling and tripling
effects on,
M5-114–M5-116
of pyramids, M5-112–M5-113
of rectangular prism vs.
rectangular pyramid,
M5-109–M5-110
of triangular prism vs.
triangular pyramid,
M5-110–M5-111

W
Whole percents, M1-168
strategies for calculating,
M1-183–M1-184

X
x-axis, M1-93, M1-102,
M3-127, M4-191
x-coordinate, M3-134

Y
y-axis, M1-102, M2-133,
M3-127, M4-191
y-coordinate, M2-133

Z
Zero, in additive inverses,
M2-32, M2-42–M2-44
Zero pairs, M2-56